*Intimacy
Sensitivity, Sex and
the Art of Love*

Intimacy

Sensitivity, Sex and the Art of Love

GINA ALLEN
and
CLEMENT G. MARTIN, M.D.

COWLES BOOK COMPANY, INC.
A Subsidiary of Henry Regnery Company

CONTENTS

PROLOGUE: THE AGE OF THE SEXUAL JOCK / vii

1 THE NEED FOR INTIMACY / 1

2 BARE FACTS / 11

3 NATURE STORY / 28

4 FROGS DON'T MAKE IT / 42

5 BODY BARRIERS TO INTIMACY / 53

6 THOUGHT LOOPS / 68

7 THE BIOLOOP / 82

8 HERE AND NOW—I AND THOU / 93

9 THE INTIMATE ENCOUNTER / 106

10 SHORT CIRCUITS / 120

11 BRIEF ENCOUNTERS / 131

12 SWAPPING AND SWINGING / 140

13 SEDUCING THE PARTNER / 150

14 THE INTIMACY SPIRAL / 159

YOUR IPQ (INTIMACY POTENTIAL QUOTIENT)

15 BECOMING—QUESTIONS / 173

16 BECOMING—ANSWERS / 187

17 BEING—QUESTIONS / 203

18 BEING—ANSWERS / 214

19   BEHAVING—QUESTIONS / 231

20   BEHAVING—ANSWERS / 242

21   MATING AND MISMATING / 261

     EPILOGUE: INTIMACY IN THE FUTURE / 276

     GLOSSARY / 279

     BIBLIOGRAPHY / 291

     INDEX / 297

Prologue:
The Age of the
Sexual Jock

We've come a long way in a brief time from the day when nobody mentioned sex in public to the present when it sometimes seems that nobody is talking about anything else. Or possibly doing anything else. Except reading about the subject. Or listening. Or watching lovemaking in the movies.

Before Kinsey, sex was a secret, shameful thing that took place in dark rooms behind closed doors, tolerated because it was necessary for procreation. Within a marriage, during the reproductive years, it might also serve as an expression of marital love, useful if it kept the family intact.

Kinsey turned on the lights in all those dark bedrooms and let the public see what went on behind the closed doors. People learned that their perfectly respectable neighbors were doing the same things about which they themselves were feeling guilty. They were enjoying sex as recreation, sometimes outside the marriage as well as within, and often in ways that had always been labeled perverted.

With this exposure of everybody's secrets a quiet, sexual evolution surfaced as a roaring revolution. As revolutions will, it turned things upside down. The sinners were elevated to saints and heroes. The sexual jock, or athlete, became the one to celebrate. And emulate. Under his tutelage sex became the nation's most popular sport. The Pill made it safe for everyone to participate.

"How many times do people do it?" is the first question college students ask lecturers who speak on sex.

If they are going to play the course they want to know what's par. They don't ask why they should play. Sexual expression is now their right. Which gives them a duty to exercise it. And when you're in there with the jocks you know a creditable performance is expected.

Unfortunately sex thrives little better under a demand for performance than it does under a cloak of shame. Either atmosphere is stifling to sexual expression which needs, after all, to express something, if only the body's healthy sexuality. You don't do that while performing, and watching and judging the performance. That's more apt to incapacitate.

Sex was never meant to be a competitive sport. It's the adult's spontaneous play, in which he gives himself to another in abandoned vulnerability and accepts the other's unquestioning trust. Though these responses facilitate the physical act of sex they are not themselves physical. They are deeply emotional. Play, particularly sexual play, involves the whole being. Physical closeness cannot be separated from emotional closeness. The personality is as much a part of the sexual act as the genitals.

It remains so even if, in the age of the sexual jock, we consider sex a purely physical need and our partners sexual objects. Sometimes sex *is* a physical need and no more. But when, in a person or a culture, sex is seldom allowed a more nurturant role, then other real needs are being ignored and one of mankind's greatest gifts squandered. We believe that this is happening in our culture—to us.

There is something schizophrenic about the new morality in which sex is celebrated as a thing apart rather than as a part of our lives. It is almost as if we didn't want our heads to know what our bodies were doing, and particularly not why.

Our bodies are aroused by pornography but our minds cannot accept this as good. They demand that the pornography have "redeeming qualities." The nude encounter group must be chaste. Adultery can be forgiven if "it didn't mean a thing."

But the mind and the body can't be separated. The mind is still the place that sexual arousal occurs, or is short-circuited. It is in the mind that most sexual incapacities originate and that psychosomatic illness feeds on the corrupt consequences of action undertaken without emotion and emotion denied physical expression. It is in the mind that loneliness and the longing for love are experienced. They are not assuaged by a physical union that ignores personalities and eschews tenderness.

The emotional need for physical closeness that also cherishes and nurtures is as basic and real as the need for sex. In this book we call that "caring contact" intimacy.

The necessity for intimacy is recognized in infants and usually catered to. After which it is labeled infantile. It is put down in little boys as "sissy" and in little girls as seductive, and deliberately discouraged by parents. After years of training in suppressing this natural yearning, neither sex is prepared as an adult either to recognize his own desire for intimacy or to fulfill the needs of others who are close to him. Not a few of our personal and social troubles stem from a lifelong frustration of our need for intimacy.

In this book we attempt to show how the lack of intimacy constricts our relationships and circumscribes our lives. More important, perhaps, the book explores the ways in which a person can relearn the art of intimacy he was untaught in childhood.

To do this, we feel, he must first know and accept himself. For he can't relate fully and honestly to others until he has sorted out the real person he is from the roles he has been assigned by society, from the ideas of his worth he has brought forward unexamined from childhood, and from the habits he has acquired of judging or ignoring, rather than experiencing people and surroundings.

To help in acquiring self-knowledge we present tested methods of concentration for reaching the primitive brain. There is also an Intimacy Potential Questionnaire with interpretations. For the reader who wants a demonstration of how quickly it is possible to change in the direction of intimacy we suggest taking the questionnaire before reading the book and again afterward. A comparison of scores (to say nothing of feelings) will provide encouragement.

Sensitivity training techniques give additional routes to self-awareness and new ways of relating to other people. The principles of sensitivity training—learning to respond to the "Here and Now and I and Thou"—are applied also to the intimate sexual encounter, with a step-by-step description of the way the pressure for performance can be eliminated and intimacy and erotic pleasure increased through the natural buildup of sensuous stimuli.

The ways in which the principles of bio-feedback apply to sexual response are presented here for the first time, in the concept of the bioloop. Readers can learn how to use bioloops to increase sexual pleasure and to alleviate sexual difficulties. With this understanding of the nature of their physical reactions, and the methods by which they can be intensified, intimate partners are able to stop concentrating on performance or worrying about failure. They are thus freed to give themselves completely to each other and to the joys of making love.

Together we as authors have a combined total of more than forty years of professional experience in the field of human and sexual relations. Gina Allen is a writer who specializes in psychology and has worked with a juvenile court and in education. Clement Martin, M.D., is a physician, the author of many books on health for the layman, and a lecturer in sex education.

From different vantage points, we have studied changing mores as they affect society and individuals. This book presents our observations and our conclusions. We hope it will contribute some knowledge to a subject that is only just beginning to be studied and researched.

We should mention two difficulties we have had with language in bringing this book into being. In discussing sex it is impossible to avoid words that some readers may find shocking, a communication barrier that is less serious between authors and readers than between intimate partners. Perhaps as sex becomes a more familiar, less highly charged subject we will be able to speak of sexual organs and functions as easily and naturally as we speak of legs and walking.

The other difficulty involves the use of pronouns. Unfortunately there is none that denotes both he and she. As is customary we have used the masculine to indicate both. But with some misgivings, and the hope that the reader will remember to apply what he reads to both sexes.

G. A.

C. G. M.

1
The Need for Intimacy

The sexual revolution has brought us to the age of the sexual jock in a game in which everyone is expected to be a competitor. The goals, rules, and scoring are controlled by the experts who also instruct in technique. Players aim for peak performance, though never quite sure from day to day what that involves. For everything keeps changing.

Once the goal was orgasm for *him* (essential for health). For *her* it was "satisfying him" (to keep him at home and preserve the marriage).

Then the goal was "satisfying her" for *him* (to prove he was a genuine sexual jock, not a run-of-the-mill athlete). *Her* goal was reaching orgasm (to prove her femininity).

To prove she was also mature it was necessary for her to reach "vaginal" orgasm. That was a change in both rules and goals that unfortunately occurred just after the men had learned to find the clitoris. At first reaching vaginal orgasm was thought to be her problem. But later it became his problem too as he was expected to keep an erection, and keep thrusting (and keep his mind off what he was doing) long enough to bring her to a mature, non-clitoral climax. Otherwise he wouldn't earn his letter.

The stakes were later raised to a mutual climax, which if you were a real jock would shake the world. This proved to be a logistics problem of some complexity and not a few players dropped by the wayside. So *he* was allowed to return to satisfying himself without regard to his partner. Quantity rather than quality became the basis for scoring, with each player pitting himself against vague and varying national averages or healthful minimum weekly requirements.

In the meantime *her* performance was to be judged in a new way—as if she were competing for the Academy Award. She wasn't required to have an orgasm. (She got as much pleasure from pleasing her partner, the experts said.) But she was required to simulate an orgasm to make *his* performance look and feel better. To keep either partner from scoring too high the experts gave *him* hints to tell if *she* was faking. Both lost points if her deception was detected.

And then came multiple orgasm. (Quantity still counts.) Now he was to give her at least three orgasms in the place of one. The first one or several could be clitoral, a preintercourse warm-up. Then a mature vaginal climax or two after intromission. And finally—back to the mutual orgasm. A truly super performance by two superjocks!

The name of the game is Sexual Freedom, because it has freed sex from the bonds of reproduction, marriage, and love. The advertised prizes are health, happiness, and an end to anxiety.

The prizes are not free. They must be earned. This is a requirement the players understand because they have been brought up to believe in the work ethic and they play their game in a society still devoted to it. Lovers are not exempted from the command to improve each shining hour. Performance is the new requirement for sexual participation. Sensuality for its own sake is still suspect.

For the dichotomous principle of a Puritan culture still applies, even if it has had to be turned around to accommodate the new separate but equal freedom of flesh and spirit. The flesh is entitled to its freedom, but only if its freedom doesn't contaminate the soul. It might be contaminated were it allowed to accompany the flesh on an uncharted exploration of sexuality.

In fact, of course, the spirit goes where the body goes and the new attempt to divide them is just as artificial as the old and therefore no more successful. As love can be rendered sterile by denial of physical expression, so lust can be twisted and warped by lack of emotional content. Freedom is incomplete and impure insofar as it is confined to the body alone.

The psychological need for meaningful contact with another human being is as great, and possibly greater, than the physical. It can't be relieved without a partner. Unrelieved, it spells anxiety, loneliness, and despair.

Physical union devoid of a caring component is no remedy for these psychological ills, whether it is sanctified by the old-fashioned marriage bond or blessed by the new sexual ethic. The inmost man is still left a beggar at the feast. He is nourished only when emotion is joined to physical passion, and spirits as well as bodies are allowed to touch in affection and mutual affirmation. That is intimacy.

Intimacy in Childhood

The need for intimacy is basic in both men and animals. On the fulfillment of this need in infancy depends our ability to function sexually in adulthood.

This was demonstrated dramatically by researchers Harry F. Harlow and Robert R. Zimmerman when they brought up baby monkeys with wire "mothers." In one experiment each infant monkey had two mothers. One, of bare wire, was the source of milk. The other was covered with cloth. The monkeys spent most of their time with the soft cloth mother, cuddling and rubbing, and would leave her reluctantly to hastily satisfy their hunger with the wire figure. Watching them, the researchers concluded that the desire for intimacy may represent a more basic instinctual force than oral or even nursing needs. And intimacy, they learned, was an essential part of an infant's sexual education.

For these monkeys raised with mother surrogates—whether of cloth or wire—who couldn't love and hold them as real mothers do, were all sexually incapable as adults. They couldn't even assume the proper postures for sexual interaction. Sex, it seems, is learned behavior. It is learned early in life through the intimate physical relationship of mother and infant.

It is easy, of course, to watch in the laboratory adult monkeys who have been deprived of intimacy in childhood and to measure their consequent inadequacies. But the results of such deprivation have also been observed in humans. Babies brought up in orphanages, where hygiene was excellent and there was plenty of good food and impersonal care, nevertheless have often sickened and died for no apparent reason. Or sometimes they have grown up mentally or emotionally incompetent. So frequent have been these reactions that researchers sought both the cause and a cure. Both were found in tenderness. When the orphanage babies were loved, hugged, cuddled, and caressed by attendants they flourished and grew normally.

One researcher studied twenty-five babies over a two-year period, measuring the amount of affectionate handling each received. Some came from deprived backgrounds and some didn't. Through the years he kept track of the children and arranged with another researcher to test them when they were teenagers.

The second researcher didn't know which of the children had been deprived of affection as babies. He did find, however, that some of the teenagers were incapable of establishing social or affectionate relationships. They turned out to be the ones who had been denied loving care as infants.

But the need for intimacy doesn't end with infancy. Psychologists have found a lack of intimate affection to be a cause of delinquency in children, nagging in wives, and infidelity in husbands. "Everyone has a psychoemotional hunger for love, cuddling, petting," says Dr. Boris Levinson, professor of psychology at Yeshiva University in New York. He finds that physical intimacy "elicits sensations of peace, quiet, and contentment."

Yet the need for intimacy is rarely acknowledged or satisfied beyond early childhood. After that we rear our offspring as if they were still the potential labor force they were in our agrarian past and in the early days of industrialization. We harden them for the duties of adulthood by withholding the affection that we fear might "spoil" them.

We block our own impulses toward tenderness by surrounding them with taboos frighteningly labeled "incest," "Oedipus complex," "homosexuality," refusing to recognize that the pathogen is not the expression of love but its denial.

To serve society's needs, or what were once its needs, we teach our young to play roles instead of allowing and helping them to develop their unique potentialities as persons. Males are trained to be aggressive and females to be submissive and dependent. Both play their parts to the detriment of their potential relationships. Antagonisms, not affection, are fostered.

The male may resent the burden of the dependent female. But when, resenting his dominance and trying to gain personhood, she attempts to step out of her subordinate role (as increasing numbers of women in the Women's Liberation movement are currently doing), he will probably resist her effort to lift the burden of herself from his unwilling shoulders. For her dependence and submission are traditional measures of his manhood. The sociological power struggle that has surfaced as a result of this conflict has long been a subterranean disruptive force in personal sexual alliances.

For men and women can't relate to each other as persons, freely and lovingly, if each must struggle against the other to maintain his socially approved position by acting his socially assigned role. The difficulties complicate the first contacts of the sexes when, in adolescence, they are drawn together by a biological need and a romantic dream.

Even then, to prove his manhood, the teenage male feels that he must make out. And to prove her virtue, with which both measure her value on the marriage mart, the female feels that she must hold out. Since both are learning sexual responses, this battle of the back seat can have lasting consequences.

Rather than learning to relax into the intimate embrace and enjoy the sensuous contact, she learns to evade, to watch with the alertness of a patrol cop, and to call a halt before the action gets out of hand. When she repeats these carefully learned ma-

neuvers in the marital bed she will be labeled, with some justifica-
tion, frigid.

In the meantime he learns to trick and intimidate, to press an
advantage and, catching her off guard, to rush toward his goal.
Dr. William H. Masters and Virginia E. Johnson, who treat
sexual inadequacies at their Reproductive Biology Research
Foundation in St. Louis, say that it takes only two or three such
pressured exposures to imprint a pattern of premature response
in the male.

Partners Without Intimacy

And so our typical teenagers, turned twenty, get married to
"live happily ever after." Neither together nor apart has either
ever experienced physical intimacy devoid of the pressure to
perform. Chances are they never will.

Inadequate as he may feel if he is unable to control his rapid
response to sexual stimulation, he is still the masterful man who
knows, instinctively, what women want. He learned it on the
street corner with the rest of his sexual expertise. "Turn them
upside down and they're all alike." "Do this and it'll drive 'em
wild." So he does "this" and "that" and everything he has been
taught that women like.

But he never makes the intimate acquaintance of this particular woman. He knows the erotic zones of the female body (he
read it in a book), but nothing at all about *her* body. Nor does
this worry him. He only worries about his own performance. He
watches her to see if he is turning her on. He watches himself,
trying to delay ejaculation. He does this by thinking of something else while performing sexually.

This refusal of sensual feelings, plus the spectator role, plus
the pressure to perform, plus the fear of inadequacy, can add
up eventually to impotence, usually not without frantic efforts

to find another partner who will cure the mounting sexual incapacity.

In the meantime the pressure for performance falls no more lightly on the woman, who comes to the sexual encounter equally burdened with handicaps. She too has learned and rehearsed patterns of sexual response, or rather of non-response, of which she would now like to rid herself. She may even know how this might be done. But she dares not take the initiative or borrow the mantle of expertise from the male for fear of stripping him of his manhood and herself of her femininity. Indeed, she too may feel that if you turn women upside down they're all alike, or were meant to be, and that her inability to respond to his un-informed overtures is further indication of her sexual inadequacy. She's not like other women and, therefore, she must be inferior.

So she turns spectator too, watching her own response. And watching him, for the time she has in which to respond depends on how well he masters his own reaction. And, in the meantime, she has learned that she has a "duty" to enhance his performance.

Whether or not he has aroused her, she must perform as if aroused. On the state of her arousal, and on the number, and/or quality, and/or timing, of the orgasms he gives her, hangs his conviction of his own sexual competency. And on these too de-pend his (and therefore her) belief in her sexual adequacy, and perhaps the continuation of the relationship.

There is nothing relaxing or erotic about attending to all these duties while engaged in a sexual embrace. In trying to will a re-sponse for the benefit of her partner the woman misses the buildup of sensuous sensations to which she should be respond-ing, at her own pace and for her own sake. As her ardor dies from lack of fuel she gives up her right to sexual satisfaction and settles for satisfying her partner by faking orgasm.

This performance on his part and play acting on hers wasn't exactly what either had in mind when they declared their love for one another. But since the only ways they have learned to relate are as role players they can't come together as persons even in their most intimate moments. So these moments that were meant to renew and affirm their love reinforce instead their roles and their crippling fears of sexual inadequacy.

The Fate of the Sexual Jock

The crippling may go beyond the sexual. The female who has learned her submissive gender role well may accumulate years of thwarted impulses toward action in her joints and muscles, which eventually retaliate with the pains and immobility of rheumatism and arthritis. The male's training as an aggressive, goal-directed, competitive, unemotional, all-American man predisposes him to ulcers and heart disease.

It isn't just that he bottles up his emotions because he can't express them, like the old American ideal, the cowboy. Emulating the new American ideal, the playboy, he has actually learned to suppress his emotions to the vanishing point. This may be more unhealthful than unexpressed emotion, says Australia's chief authority on heart disease, Dr. Salik Minc. Actions without emotions burden the heart more than emotion without action, he has found.

Many individual couples and groups are trying to establish intimate and honest equality between the sexes without role playing. Yet society in general regards all these attempts with suspicion. The search for a new kind of freedom and equality is thought to be freakish, rather than a sincere attempt to bring honesty into the world.

A colorful segment of the current generation of youth has succeeded in giving up roles in every sphere but the sexual. There the long-haired male, who has forsaken his father's dress, ambitions, and way of life, clings still to the traditional masculine role. Whether his devotion is to drugs, religion, or revolution, the love he proclaims is for *man*kind.

In radical headquarters across the country women serve and men are served. In hippie camps a woman is either a "chick" who belongs to all men or a "lady" who belongs to one. In religious groups, whether Eastern or Western, women are assigned their traditional, subservient positions. The female followers of Krishna are given "master-mates" and are taught that babies that take female forms are inferior and meant to serve men. However warm the relationship between master and servant, it is not as emotionally involving as a love between equals. Nor can it be the person-to-person relationship essential for intimacy. The young have found it easier to shed their gray flannel suits than their sex roles.

Most have not gone that far. Sociologists tell us that middle America is still filled with young men devoted to the competitive ambition that motivated their fathers. And to the double standard that rules the older generation's sexual relations. The young man cut in this traditional mold prides himself on exploiting women with strong sex drives, using their needs to satisfy his own.

Then he marries the "good" girl, preferably a virgin, with few sexual needs of her own. He exploits her by making it her wifely duty to act without emotion in physically gratifying him. He protects this union by reverting to courtship patterns in his extramarital affairs. He counts himself as faithful if his outside sexual trysts "don't really mean a thing." Yet he can pay dearly for his illicit pleasure.

Most of the heart patients brought into hospital emergency rooms in the middle of the night are middle-aged men who suffered their attacks, not in their own beds, but in strange beds with women other than their wives. Whether their hearts were overloaded with the emotion of guilt or with sexual activity for which they were unprepared emotionally is by then an academic question.

They are only the most obvious casualties among the sexual jocks. For actually everybody loses when sex becomes goal-oriented, exploitive, and competitive. The greatest thing couples lose is the chance to fulfill their deep and very basic need for intimacy. It is doubtful if even the common cold causes as much misery as this particular deficiency in our lives. Loneliness is all too often our lot in the age of the sexual jock.

It need not be. We could relate to each other in physical and emotional intimacy if we would take off our coats of armor and become vulnerable, one to another, as humans rather than super-beings and as individuals rather than sexual role players.

Opening the avenues to intimacy means tearing down the cultural roadblocks that have been erected against it. It means giving up roles and becoming one's self. For only as a real, thinking, feeling person can one relate to another. Only when one has learned to know and accept the self as worthy and valuable does one have a gift of worth to offer another. Only when one has learned to love one's self can one learn to love another.

Tearing down the roadblocks means eliminating our fears of emotional, non-game-playing contact with others. It means discarding both the romantic myth of the "one and only" and the equally fallacious idea that "there is no wrong one." It means the end of exploitive sex without feeling, both in marriage and in one-night stands. It means the acceptance of the genitals as an attractive part of the body, and the acceptance of the body, mind, and emotions as erotic participants in the sex act.

Intimacy means throwing away the rules that make for rigidity, and relearning the spontaneity of early childhood. It means throwing away the fear of inadequacy and accepting ourselves, and the other, with all our limitations. It means giving up the goal of bigger and better orgasms and relaxing into the enjoyment of every sensuous pleasure of every intimate caress.

Above all, intimacy means sharing with each other not only our bodies but our hearts. Sex as a competitive sport can become boring and meaningless. As the language of intimacy it enriches life.

2
Bare Facts

Neither sex is biologically "pure." Each contains some of the other. Recent investigators have been more impressed with the ways in which males and females are alike than with their differences. And they've found more striking psychological differences between members of the same sex than between males and females generally.

This uniqueness of each individual, whether male or female, provides the wide range of human potential that makes change and progress possible. If each of us passed on to our offspring only maleness and femaleness we might, like dogs and cattle, make handsome specimens for a show ring. But we wouldn't have reached the moon—either in space capsules or in intimate embrace.

What happens in an intimate embrace that is destined to produce another human being is that the egg and the sperm of two highly individual persons combine to program another completely different human being. At the moment they combine, the cell they create is instantly either male or female. Different, but with many similarities.

For one thing, whether male or female, this budding embryo contains an X chromosome, which it received from the egg. If it is female it also has an X chromosome from the sperm. If it is male it contains a Y chromosome from the sperm. As the embryo grows each new cell receives a duplicate of the chromosome heritage. As adults, the fully developed male and female, looking quite different, will be alike in that each will have at least one X chromosome in every cell of the body.

Though the embryo is chromosomatically either male or female from the moment of conception, its sex is not immediately apparent. The gonads, the sexual glands within the pelvic cavity, are alike in both sexes. So is a little bump, called the genital eminence, that appears between the navel and the tail. As this tissue grows it spreads outward, flaring into a buttress at the sides and rising in a nodule, the genital tubercle, at the upper end. Longitudinal folds and grooves begin to mark this tissue. The center groove is the urethral, protected by a fold on either side. On the outer edges of the buttresses labio-scrotal swellings appear and form folds.

For weeks these developments are the same in both sexes. Then the genital tubercle develops into the glans penis in the male or the glans clitoris in the female. In the male the urethral folds meet to close off the urethra and the buttresses join to become the shaft of the penis. In the female the urethral folds become the labia minora, or inner lips, of the vulva and the buttress area next to them deepens to become the vestibule of the vagina.

It is eleven weeks before it is possible to tell the boys from the girls in the womb. And it is seven months before the gonads are differentiated. Then in the male they descend into the labio-scrotal folds, which become the male scrotum, protecting these developing testicles. The same gonads in the female remain in place in the pelvis and develop as ovaries, while the labio-scrotal folds become the labia majora, or outer lips, of the female genitals.

By the time the baby is born the external genitals are so distinctly male or female that it is possible to tell the child's sex at a glance. After that, likenesses are ignored and differences accentuated. We are taught to be males and females and to express our gender in ways determined by the society into which we were born.

Studies done at the Endocrine Clinic at Johns Hopkins Hospital in Baltimore have shown that hermaphrodites born with some of the reproductive organs of both sexes adopt the gender to which they are assigned at birth. Reared as girls they grow into women, psychologically and sexually. If they are brought up as boys they grow into men, with a completely male orientation and identification. Plastic surgery and hormone treatments bring them the rest of the way to full sexuality.

When babies are born their genitals are sometimes considerably enlarged as a result of the mother's secretion of hormones, and when this is coupled with abnormalities in the genitals it can lead to mis-sexing of the child—in about one case in 10,000. Researchers have found that boys who were miscalled girls at birth, and raised as girls, continue to think of themselves as feminine and to behave as women, despite beards and penises. And despite the lack of these attributes, women reared as males think of themselves as male through a lifetime.

The researchers have concluded from their observations that the child is born psychologically sexually neutral and that he "becomes psychologically differentiated as masculine or feminine in the course of the many experiences of growing up."

It is this psychological neutrality at birth that makes sex roles flexible, so that they can meet the varied needs of different cultures. In America males are brought up to be practical and stoic. Females are allowed to be scatterbrained and emotional. Traditionally in Persia the reverse has been true. Females have been taught to be cool and hardheaded. Males have been permitted to be flighty and to cry in public, even as adults.

Just how we learn to identify and behave as males or females isn't known, but the crucial period for learning seems to be in the first years of life, before parents realize that they are teaching these important lessons. And indeed their teaching is completely unconscious. Somehow, as we are fed and held and loved, we learn our sex roles—and we learn intimacy.

Chemical Messengers

In our early years hormones do little to differentiate the male and the female. For until just before puberty the production of sexual hormones is low, and there's not much difference between those coursing through the bodies of the little boy and the little girl.

Even when the sexual hormones up their production at puberty they aren't immediately discriminatory. Everybody makes both male and female hormones his whole life long. The estrogens, or female hormones, that cause girls' breasts to grow initially do the same thing for boys. And the androgens, or male hormones, that cause boys to borrow dad's razor produce the beginnings of mustaches in young women.

Eventually men produce more androgens than estrogens, and women more female hormones than male hormones. But all our lives long each of us produces hormones of the opposite sex as well as the hormones of our own. Testosterone, the chief male hormone, which controls the pigmentation of the skin, is responsible not only for the beautiful tan a young man gets on the beach, but also for the beautiful tan of his girl friend. And sometimes for two cases of acne.

Besides their role in sexual and reproductive development and activity, the sex hormones perform other important functions in both sexes. The male hormones influence height and strengthen muscles. They also contribute to mental alertness and memory. Female estrogens strengthen bones and act as psychological energizers that provide resistance to fatigue.

Estrogens are produced cyclically not only in women but also in men. British scientists discovered this when they were investigating the possibility that an excess of female hormones might be responsible for homosexuality. They found that, indeed, homosexual men produced estrogens cyclically, as did females. But so did the heterosexual male controls. And so did the scientists themselves.

A fall in the estrogen level in either sex can cause a mood deflation. Since women have higher estrogen levels than men, their monthly mood swing is more pronounced. And the drop in hormones triggers menstruation.

But this is not a one-way street. Emotions also affect hormone production. Worry about whether or not a menstrual period is going to be on schedule can produce it ahead of time or postpone it indefinitely. So can the tenseness brought on by an examination or the excitement of a new love affair.

Sex hormone production is controlled by the master pituitary gland. In turn, the pituitary receives chemical messages from the hypothalamus, the emotional center and root of the brain.

When you meet someone attractive and desirable your central nervous system records this fact. "I am really being turned on," is the message that the hypothalamus receives. It relays this information to the glands and they turn you on even more by increasing the production of sex hormones. Or the message can start with the glands as, "I want to be turned on," and travel via the hypothalamus to the central nervous system, which sets you in motion looking for that someone.

Either way, the gonads increase the production of sex hormones which firm women's breasts and men's muscles, strengthen bones, and contribute to mental and physical well-being. Sex, you see, gives you many gifts besides pleasure.

One of these gifts not generally recognized or used is relief from premenstrual tension. Premenstrual tension is really a syndrome of emotional and physical factors that may include a tendency to retain water in body tissues and cramps from the uterine contractions that force the menstrual fluids out of the womb. A congestion of blood in the pelvic region can also produce an uncomfortable feeling of aching heaviness.

This vasocongestion is physically identical with the congestion that occurs in the latest phase of sexual excitement, just prior to orgasm. Just as orgasm relieves the condition at that time, so, for many women, orgasm also relieves discomfort at the time of menstruation. Orgasm, whether achieved through masturbation or intercourse, eliminates cramps and lessens vasocongestion and emotional tension.

Controlling Conception

Premenstrual tension also has been eliminated for millions of women by the oral contraceptive pill. But for an unlucky 10 percent of the six or seven million women on the Pill, menstrual discomfort has been increased.

These varied reactions to the Pill are to be expected. It is potent medicine, not to be taken lightly. A thorough examination by a physician is needed to determine whether or not a woman can take the Pill and which one of many different kinds would be best for her. Follow-up examinations are a must for women on oral contraception so that any adverse side effects can be quickly noted and dealt with.

The Pill works by keeping the level of female hormones in the body high, as they are in pregnancy. This is believed to offer several different kinds of protection against conception. The high hormonal level is supposed to suppress ovulation. But even if ovulation occurs, the hormones change the rate at which the Fallopian tubes move the egg from the ovary to the womb. And they change the climate of the uterus so that the egg is rejected rather than implanted. At the same time the progestins in the Pill affect the mucus secreted by the cervix, making it inhospitable to sperm and perhaps reducing the sperm's capacity to fertilize.

The oral contraceptive pill is not an ideal method of birth control, nor is it 100 percent effective. But it's the most reliable pregnancy preventer we have today. Fortunately, a majority of women seem to be able to take the Pill without complications. Adverse side effects can include irregular bleeding, blood clotting, high blood pressure, headaches, depression, interference with vision, nervousness, temporary hair thinning, pigment spots on the skin, and weight gain.

Though there has been a decrease in cancer of the cervix since women have been taking the Pill, and no increase in cancer of the breast, women who are considered cancer risks are generally not given the Pill. Neither are young girls whose growth is not completed, because the Pill can stunt growth by prematurely closing the growth ends of the bones.

For women who can't take the Pill there are other methods of birth control, though all are less effective. One is the intrauterine device (IUD). This consists of a plastic coil or loop that is fitted into the uterus by a doctor. Once in place it can protect against conception for years, for its presence in the uterus somehow prevents implantation of the fertilized egg.

The presence of a foreign body in the uterus will also cause the uterus to expel an egg not yet firmly implanted. In their *Abortion Handbook* Patricia Maginnis and Lana Clark Phelan report that some women use this fact to get abortions from their doctors or at Planned Parenthood clinics. The minute they fear they are pregnant they rush down to have a loop or coil inserted as a contraceptive device. Doctors try to avoid inserting the IUD in women already pregnant by insisting that the woman report to the office during, or at the end of, her period. Blood from a slice of liver, however, can simulate menstruation quite convincingly. The problem with the IUD as either an abortifacient or a contraceptive device is that in some women the uterus ejects the implement.

The failure rate for the most commonly prescribed oral contraceptive is less than one pregnancy per year for every hundred women on the Pill. The failure rate for the IUD is twice that. For the next most effective contraceptive method, the diaphragm, the failure rate jumps to ten pregnancies per hundred women per year.

The rubber diaphragm is carefully fitted by a physician, who instructs the woman how to place it in the vagina before intercourse so that one end covers the mouth of the uterus, with the lower edge tucked beneath the pubic bone to keep it in place. During sexual excitement, however, the inner two thirds of the vagina balloon outward so that the diaphragm no longer fits snugly. Sperm, and even the penis itself, can then come between it and the mouth of the uterus it is supposed to protect.

At that time any and all protection comes from the spermicidal jelly or cream with which the diaphragm has been daubed before insertion. Some spermicidal agents have a contraceptive reliability equal to that of the diaphragm. They come packaged in foams or in aerosol cans, so that they are easy to use. And some of them, in some states, can be bought in drugstores without prescriptions.

Less reliable methods of birth control include the condom, the douche, the rhythm method, and coitus interruptus. Any of these measures is better than nothing in an emergency, but none of them should be counted on continuously to avoid the emergency of unwanted pregnancy. "Ninety percent of all people," warns Dr. Edris Rice-Wray, "are caused by accidents."

In his currently popular book, *Everything You Always Wanted to Know About Sex*, Dr. David Reuben apparently recommends sticking a foaming bottle of Coca-Cola into the vagina as an emergency contraceptive technique. This is not only useless as contraception, but extremely dangerous. All douches are equally ineffective in preventing fertilization. The sperm are long gone from the scene by the time the douching liquid arrives—they are up in the tubes doing their thing.

The danger of using a liquid-gas mixture such as Coke, or any carbonated soft drink, is that the pressure can rupture interior anatomy. If the gas gets into the uterus, it may enter a blood vessel and cause an air embolism. An embolism can lead to death if it enters the brain or collapses the lung. Both are very real potential hazards.

Coca-Cola presents another hazard, known to every garage mechanic. It is an extremely acid solution, great for removing rusty bumper bolts. This much acidity is not abnormal—in the stomach—but that's the only place any soft drink belongs!

The Breast and the Penis

At puberty, and for several years thereafter, most people have a built-in method of birth control. They are sterile. The first ejaculations of the male contain few or no sperm. And a majority of women begin to menstruate before they start to ovulate or to produce the hormones necessary to attach a fertilized ovum to the uterine wall.

This is the reason that in societies in which sex play, including intercourse, is allowed prior to marriage, illegitimate children are still very rare. This period of adolescent sterility is not exclusively a human phenomenon. It occurs in other animals too, apparently as a natural protection against pregnancy before maturity. It is not a completely dependable protection, however. In some instances females start to ovulate before their first menstruation. And sterile periods vary in duration from individual to individual.

The sterile period occurs because sexual maturity is a slow rather than a sudden process, and highly variable from person to person. Many of our feelings of sexual inferiority come from this period when we think ourselves adults but are really in a transitory stage. It is then that a girl begins to worry about the size of her breasts and a boy about the size of his penis. These sexual organs will attain full size with maturity, which comes usually in the early twenties.

Human female breasts are unusual in the animal world in that they do grow along with the growing pubescent female. In most animals the breasts increase in size only at the end of pregnancy, as they prepare to deliver milk to the offspring. When nursing has ceased, they recede again until they are needed for milk production another time.

Human breasts also increase in size with pregnancy and with the production of milk that follows parturition. And sexual stimulation produces temporary increases of up to 25 percent in overall breast size, while the nipples erect and expand in diameter and length, as they do during nursing. Apart from silicone injections, which may induce cancer, these temporary enlargements are the only measures that really increase breast size.

The expansion of the female breast is an obvious indication of sexual interest, as is the erection of the male penis. This has led males (in our culture) to assume, erroneously, that the larger the breast the greater the sexual capacity. And some anthropologists have suggested that the permanently enlarged breast of the human female developed originally as a sexual signal to attract the male.

This assumes that throughout human history men have been breast worshippers, as they obviously are in our culture today. Witness the commercial exploitation of the breasts in advertisements, magazines, movies, and nightclubs. Do the pragmatic moneymakers know something the psychologists have been afraid to investigate?

Men want breasts. They buy magazines and newspapers to look at them. They flock to movies, musicals, and topless restaurants and nightclubs to see them. In order to fondle them they pay large-breasted call girls more than their less well-endowed competitors, and date and marry large-breasted women. The result has been a demand for breast enlargement not only by those who make their living by displaying their mammary glands, but also by ordinary women who don't want to be handicapped in the competition for sexual partners.

But what indeed does this emphasis on breasts signify? Nothing less than breast envy on the part of the male. He wants breasts—an impossible dream. So he seeks to acquire them by acquiring the female who possesses them. This is the way people fall in love, according to Theodore Reik. First they envy and hate the one who possesses the attributes they desire. Then they incorporate these attributes by falling in love with the possessor.

The breast is, after all, the first comforter of the infant after he is expelled from the warm security of the womb to the insecurity of the outer world. The breast likewise is denied him after a few months, but in that short time he has identified with it. This feminine identification persists long after removal from the breast. Even at two and one half years of age most little boys in America give the wrong answer to the question, "Are you a boy or a girl?" Not until age three have they reconciled themselves to a breastless existence as a male. And even at age four they cling to the idea that gender can be changed.

Though breast envy is evident everywhere around us, it is only the surface manifestation of a deeper envy of the female's biological role. When physiological measurements are taken of male anxiety, questions about the wish to be a female and to make babies produce high anxiety reactions. Dr. Anita I. Bell, who has pioneered in this research, finds that though they can be physiologically recorded, these anxieties aren't usually consciously perceived. This could, she feels, "explain the generalized oversight on the part of males about this area in the studies of the male, which for the most part are done by males."

mate or a little brother isn't large and impressive. It's small and insubstantial.

The sexual organs that are both strikingly visible and of large proportion are the breasts of the mother, which are apparent even when she is fully clothed. Let us follow Freud's example and theorize that these are what excite the envy of children of both sexes, and that they would like to possess those breasts again as they did as suckling babes. The little girl knows that one day she will have her own breasts. The little boy forever yearns for them.

It does not invalidate Freud's remarkable contribution to our understanding of human psychology to point out that he was human, fallible, and deeply imbued with a patriarchal attitude—still prevalent in society today. He was also prey to the usual male anxieties about female biological functions, which seem, in his case, to have been so deep that to relieve them he found it necessary to strip the female of all biological purpose but the incubation of the "penis child." Not only is her anatomy insufficient, but so is her libido and her reproductive drive. The perpetuation of the species, says Freud, "has been dependent upon the aggressiveness of the male, independent of the woman's consent."

Only by investing the penis with all woman's natural functions was Freud able to make its possession a mark of superiority to be envied by the woman, who was robbed to enhance its importance. No wonder he assumes that she is envious! Considered in this light, Freud's theory of penis envy has much to tell us about male sexual anxieties and the way they have affected the relationship between the sexes.

If penis envy exists, it certainly does not have the implications Freud gave it but seems, rather, to be an exclusively male trait. Though the human male has the largest erect penis of any primate, most men worry a good deal about the size of their own organs in comparison to others. They equate a larger organ with greater potency and envy the sexual advantage. Quite unnecessarily.

The largest penis ever recorded was measured by the French anatomist, Dr. Adrien Sharpy, in 1890. It was 13¾ inches long.

The man who possessed it was a victim of acromegalia, a pituitary disorder that causes enlargement of the extremities. It also causes impotence.

Penile size has little to do with body size either. Measuring the organs of 312 men, Masters and Johnson found the largest flaccid penis on a man 5 feet 8 inches tall, weighing 152 pounds. His penis was 5.5 inches in length. The smallest flaccid penis, slightly over 2⅓ inches, belonged to a man almost 6 feet tall, who weighed 178 pounds. Since a penis that is small when limp expands much more than a larger organ, both could be close to the same size when erect.

All the worrying men have done about penile size hasn't changed dimensions through the centuries. Measurements extrapolated from drawings and models found in ancient Egyptian tombs show penises of about 5 inches in length. Drawings on Greek vases give a range of from 5¼ inches to 7 inches. The famous Indian *Kama Sutra,* written in A.D. 200, lists sizes from 2½ inches to slightly over 7 inches. More recently, 4,500 measurements obtained by Kinsey showed that 90 percent of male organs measure from 5 to 7½ inches in length, with a diameter of 1¼ to 1½ inches.

There are several reasons a smaller penis might be preferred to a larger one, by both men and women. Though the vagina can expand enough to accommodate a baby's head during delivery, it is ordinarily only about 3 inches long, S-shaped rather than cylindrical, and about an inch in diameter. When sexually stimulated it is capable of expanding in diameter to almost 2½ inches and in length to about 4 inches. Engorgement of the labia increases the total length of the canal to 6 inches at the height of sexual excitement.

Contrary to medical folklore, a penis longer than this can cause discomfort to the female partner in intercourse by hitting against the cervix during deep thrusting. Nor does the sensitive glans of the penis receive much stimulus in the inner depths of the canal where the vaginal walls balloon out during sexual excitement so that they have little or no contact with the glans.

Close contact is maintained only in the muscled and sensitive entrance of the vagina. Here the vagina can stimulate the glans of the smaller penis but only the comparatively insensitive shaft of the larger organ. It is quite possible that men with small members have—and give—more exciting sensations during intercourse than their more generously endowed brothers.

Since women's sexual organs are hidden, except for the breasts, they've not caused nearly the anxiety that men's organs have. Women worry a lot about the size and shape of their breasts, but many women aren't even curious about their genitals and worry only that they may be different from those of other women. And so they are.

The vulva is as individual as the face. And like the face, it reflects age and experiences and feelings. During sexual excitement, in the young woman who has not had a child, the labia minora turn from pink to a bright red. In the older woman who has had children the color changes from dull red to burgundy during sexual stimulation. With continuing sexual experience the color of the inner lips grows permanently darker and the lips themselves expand, frequently protruding through the labia majora.

If we had grown up in Bali, our mothers, and other adults, would have stroked our genitals as infants, saying, "Pretty! Pretty!" if we were girls, and "Handsome! Handsome!" if we were boys. In the United States such behavior on the part of an adult could result in a prison sentence.

Consequently, few of us have ever been told that our genitals are pretty or handsome. Nor do we feel that they are. Worse, we don't feel they are really part of us, like our legs and our arms. From childhood they have been cut off from our view and our consciousness. We accept them, reluctantly and momentarily, for sexual activity. But they aren't part of the body image.

To test this, strip in front of a full-length mirror and look at both your genitals and your face. Men can do this standing up. Women can do it best propped on pillows, half reclining on the floor before a full-length mirror, until both genitals and face can be seen at the same time.

Does this make you uncomfortable? Do you want to cover your genitals quickly and forget them? The more you feel this way the more important it is that you incorporate your genitals into your self-image. You can't use them well in sexual encounters if you reject or despise them. Look at them until they become as familiar and accepted as your face. And as much a part of you. Feel them, stroke them, learn to know them.

You recognize the beauty of flowers, which are the reproductive parts of plants. Your flowers are no less lovely. Why should you continue to think they are inferior simply because the significant adults in your childhood, unlike the Balinese, ignored your genitals and allowed you to be ashamed of them? People who take pride in their sexual organs, and accept happily the pleasure they can give, have the best possible preparation for a joyful intimate relationship.

Human Pair Bonding

Because humans belong to a pair-bonding species, our intimate relationships usually begin during adolescence and are legalized in an "until death do us part" marriage contract. This contract is based on the natural tendency of the human to fall in love with one partner and stay paired through the birth and infancy of the offspring. Like the graylag goose, we're a pair-bonding species. Very early in our history human groups took advantage of this biological fact, made it the basis of social organization, and placed it under social control.

Problems then were quite different from ours today. Prey to famine and disease, which kept decimating and threatening to eradicate small populations, men made marriage and breeding mandatory, and stretched pair bonding to include polygamy when extra women of breeding age were available. Many religions sponsored erotic exhibitions and orgies to stimulate underfed males who might otherwise grow sexually lethargic. Non-reproductive sex, including the use of Onan's method of birth control, coitus interruptus, or spilling the seed on the ground, became a sin.

Death by the age of thirty-five was the norm for mankind until 1850. Couples married at puberty, or soon afterward, but men outlived women, who frequently died in childbirth. And so, in his brief married life, a man might have several wives even if he was married to only one at a time. No single pair bond was required to last more than a few years.

The need for population was increased over the centuries by the demands of wars and colonization, and finally by the coming of the industrial revolution. The need wasn't met, even when improved living conditions and increased medical knowledge brought a gradual extension of the life span in industrial countries, and with it a longer period of years devoted to marriage and breeding. So marital, reproductive sex continued to be the only sexual outlet that had social approval.

By 1950 life expectation in the United States had risen to more than sixty-eight years. And though the age for marriage had been postponed until eighteen or twenty, the union lasted for almost half a century. Through the early years the pair bond was reinforced by the responsibilities of child rearing. In the later years it was expected to operate unaided.

Now that an expanding population is considered a liability rather than a necessity, the biological pair bond will have few reinforcements throughout marriages contracted to last five and six decades. Quite possibly it isn't strong enough to endure under these circumstances. Yet society gives no help or approval to efforts to adapt marriage to a changed world. Nor does it encourage the sexual education and techniques that might strengthen the pair bond of which it now demands so much.

3
Nature Story

If we did what comes naturally, we would be at home in our own bodies, free to let them breathe in the open air, to move them and let them move us, to touch them and feel their living, to explore the ways they can bring us joy. If we did what comes naturally, our minds and hearts and bodies would be reciprocal gifts for those we love. We would touch and be touched by them, emotionally and physically, and learn the ways we can bring each other joy.

One reason we don't do what comes naturally is that we are taught that it's unnatural.

It's unnatural, say the arbiters, to delight in our own nude bodies or the nude bodies of others. It's exhibitionism, voyeurism, immature, and sick. It is also against the law.

It's unnatural, say the arbiters, to derive pleasure from our own bodies. This is a sign of maladjustment, immaturity, and possibly neurosis. Particularly if autoeroticism is carried on "to excess," or beyond the age of twenty.

It's unnatural, say the arbiters, to make physical love to a member of one's own family or sex. One can be confined to a mental institution or a penal institution for such unnatural acts.

It's unnatural, say the arbiters, to make physical love to anybody, even one's own wife, except through natural, reproductive penile-vaginal contact. In many legal codes, oral and anal intercourse are labeled "crimes against nature."

It is "unnatural" to instruct a child—even a sexually active adolescent—about the part of life that most concerns him unless the instruction is given verbally by his parents. It is "unnatural" for an adult actually to teach the child how to make love or to let him watch sexual activity, even in movies, or to give him books in which he can read graphic descriptions of physical lovemaking. Though one might think it would be a crime to force children to grow up in such ignorance of one of their most important functions, instead, the adult who instructs in socially unapproved ways can be accused of perpetrating a crime against the child.

All of these "unnatural" acts consist of doing what comes naturally. So obviously they can't be truly unnatural. None of man's erotic activities are, says Dr. Earle M. Marsh of the University of California Medical Center in San Francisco. Every one of man's sexual variations is also found in nature. *Homo sapiens* just aren't as ingenious or as wicked as they like to think they are.

Birds and Bees Do It

Most of our sexuality, except the reproductive, has been labeled unnatural because that's the tag that frightens modern man. Science is his new superstition. He's given up theology for biology and psychology. He no longer fears going to hell but he very much fears being unnatural or abnormal. What he fails to notice is that the sexual prohibitions that have been given him in the name of science are the same ones that used to be labeled sins. And it is the prohibitions that are unnatural.

Young animals engage freely in sex play, as anyone who has ever raised kittens or puppies knows. In this way they educate themselves for their future sexual roles. The education includes masturbation, mutual masturbation, watching adults copulate, and trying to imitate their behavior, often with members of the same sex.

Nor does the play stop with maturity, when serious reproductive sex begins. To maintain a species, the sexual attractions of one sex for the other must be strong. But the sex drive itself must be stronger and undifferentiated, for it cannot be allowed to die just because of adverse mating conditions. According to the rules of nature, sexual creatures seek whatever outlets are available.

The animal kingdom shows us the entire range of sexual activity—all of it quite natural. Spiders masturbate. Elephants do too—the males using their trunks, the females getting help from their sisters. Primates, the sexiest of all animal groups, use their hands. Lack of a hand is no drawback to male deer and antelope, who use antler rubbing to stimulate extrusion of the penis, complete with ejaculation. Some rub their antlers against trees, others plunge them into the ground. Dolphins have been observed using a strong stream of water directed at the genitals for autoerotic entertainment. All these behavior patterns are found in the adults as well as the young—often serving as a change from regular heterosexual behavior.

Anyone who has been on a cattle ranch during the mating season knows that the field is wide open. Bulls mount bulls, cows mount and thrust at other cows, cows mount the small bulls. And, occasionally, bull and cow meet in the approved, mature manner. Other animals, according to research, become so bored with one sex partner that they stop all sex activity. If a new partner is introduced, everything begins again—at the same pace as was seen in the first mating process.

Young male apes are frequently denied access to females in their society by the older males, who surround themselves with harems. Until these adults die, or become weak enough to be overpowered, the younger males find sexual outlet through sodomizing each other. If two male rams are penned away from the ewes of the flock they also trade sexual favors with one another. Animals denied appropriate mates will copulate and set up housekeeping with animals of another kind. Lions and tigers can produce offspring, tigrons, from their unions. Other species mate without conception, or with such a low degree of fertility that the offspring never survive gestation.

Jealousy is common among some animals, and unknown in others. Wolves are particularly persnickety, according to Benson E. Ginsburg of the University of Chicago. A female may not allow some males to mount her at all. Others she will tolerate. If her heart's desire is copulating with another female she may—even while mounted—attempt to break up the other couple! Foxes won't even look at another partner once they have selected the "right one." They stay faithful for the entire year, once they have mated.

Child care also does not have the rigid structure in the animal kingdom that some sociologists would call natural. The seahorse role in sex is a complete reversal from the usual. The female has a protruding sex member, the ovipositor. With this she forces eggs into the abdominal pouch of the male where they receive his sperm, and he maintains the pregnancy. Birth is apparently quite a difficult time for him as he bumps around trying to dislodge, or deliver his 150 to 200 offspring.

Equal sharing in the family problems is the "modern" psychology of wolves. The male and female both provide food for the young, by regurgitating the partially digested food they have eaten on the hunt. In some groups of birds the female frequently wanders off, leaving the male with the entire job of hatching and feeding the young. Sometimes he does; sometimes he wanders off too. Other birds, such as the cuckoo, foist the raising of their young on others by the simple trick of laying their eggs in another bird's nest. Often the unfortunate original tenants are neglected by their parents, busy feeding the intruder.

Sexual orgies are common among the howler monkeys, when parties of females in heat wear out several males in bursts of sexual activity that far exceed reproductive necessity. Prostitution also occurs among primates, when females and subordinate males in a group will offer themselves sexually in exchange for food and physical protection. Even cruelty, including maiming and killing, sometimes accompanies sexual congress in nature.

Since all man's sexual variations occur elsewhere in the animal kingdom we can't properly label them unnatural. Rather, some are socially unacceptable. And some, such as sadistic rape, are socially insupportable. The suppression of natural manifestations that threaten the survival of the group is a necessary control that occurs among animals and primitive peoples as well as in our own society.

When controls are used unnecessarily, however, they themselves may endanger the group by forcing unnatural conditions on strong biological drives. Many of our own sexual restrictions date back to the moral codes of the ancient Hebrews, Babylonians, and Assyrians. Useful then, perhaps, many of them no longer meet the needs of individuals or of society.

Everybody Does It

When, in the nineteenth century, we took away from young people the right to marry at puberty we also took away from them all rights to legitimate sexual expression. We segregated them in single gender schools, where the only possible sexual learning was autoerotic or homophile. Homosexuality had already been labeled a sin. Autoeroticism soon became considered both a sin and a sickness.

This happened with the publication in France, in 1860, of a book called *Onana—A Treatise on the Diseases Produced by Onanism.* In it the author, a Dr. Tissot, erroneously identified the Onanism prohibited in the Bible with masturbation. That made masturbation a sin. For good measure, Dr. Tissot also held masturbation responsible for many dread maladies, including insanity.

The book was widely accepted. The English translation alone went through eighty editions. Masturbation was denounced from the pulpit. Doctors tried a variety of cures and preventive measures, including locking the testicles of young men in spiked cages at night, surgical removal of the clitoris in women, and incarceration of offenders in mental institutions.

We now know that masturbation is an important sexual outlet for people deprived of partners. It not only contributes to their well-being but prevents many minor and major transgressions of society's sexual code. For young people it performs a valuable educational function, teaching them the ways in which their bodies provide and respond to sexual pleasure.

In his famous study of sex in America, Dr. Alfred Kinsey and his researchers found that people who had masturbated most frequently in adolescence were the ones who made the best sexual adjustments in marriage. More recently, Masters and Johnson have included masturbation and mutual masturbation in their therapy with sexually inadequate couples.

Though masturbation would appear to be one of mankind's blessings, the anxiety makers still insist on surrounding it with shame and guilt. Like many other sexual pleasures, it is pronounced "immature." And even the immature are warned not to do it to excess, without being given any criteria for judging how much is too much. The result for most people is more anxiety. Few are wise enough to trust their bodies, as did the young man who told his adult adviser: "You can't do it too much 'cause if you do you can't do it no more."

Masturbation is a highly individual act. It is somewhat standardized in men, who often learn to masturbate in adolescence when they are instructed in the technique by older boys. Adolescent masturbation in teenage males is often a group experience. It is rarely so with females, who discover the pleasure by themselves and indulge in it alone. No two women observed in research laboratories have an identical method of automanipulation. And each man too develops his own individual technique and response pattern.

For this reason each intimate partner should be aware of the autoerotic mechanism of the other. Observing and participating in your partner's sexual patterns of autostimulation is the only way to really learn them. This will improve both verbal and nonverbal communication and enhance the sensuous joy of the relationship. By this means intimates will find out what pleases the partner during sexual play. No one is upset if his partner says, "Please scratch my back, up here, over there, harder—now softer." Yet the same explicit instructions about sexual techniques are often considered taboo. They should not be.

For those who haven't permanent sexual partners it is helpful to know how members of the opposite sex give themselves sensuous pleasure. Then you are better equipped to please when you are doing the giving.

Most men use manual manipulation when they masturbate. Variations are possible using bedclothes, pillow, or pressing against an object after an erection has been obtained. The loose skin on the shaft of the penis may be manipulated back and forth by hand, and the glans never touched. Often the enjoyment of this is enhanced by using a moisturizing lotion or cream. The pressure used may be very light for one individual and intense for another. Orgasm can be produced in this manner without ever touching the glans, the most sensitive part of the penis. Sometimes the glans is included in the overall hand movement. At other times only the glans is manipulated. Then less pressure is used because of the great sensitivity of this part of the man's sexual organ.

Males are not able to bring themselves to orgasm by fantasy alone, but nearly all report some fantasy accompanying auto-manipulation. Fantasies may be elaborate, or as simple as an imagined lover, sometimes inspired by a picture in a magazine. Often there is a desire to ejaculate on the picture—a part of completing the fantasy.

When a man dies by hanging, ejaculation almost always occurs, according to forensic pathologists. Some men flirt with death by short periods of strangulation for this effect. Sometimes this flirtation leads to death. Reducing the supply of blood to the brain often produces ejaculation. Boys, tireless in seeking fresh methods of masturbation, have found various ways of accomplishing this, all of them dangerous.

Males also use various mechanical devices for masturbation, some of them rather dangerous, as physicians called for assistance will testify. A dildo in the rectum can give some stimulation to both heterosexual and homosexual males. Many of these devices are battery-operated and are said to be both underpowered and undersized for their intended purpose. Inserting objects into the urethra is also an autoerotic practice. This leads, occasionally, to loss of objects in the bladder—once again, a situation requiring medical help. Clinical thermometers, catheters, and other long narrow instruments seem to be frequently chosen. Certainly, they have frequently been recovered.

In our agrarian past many boys used animals for sexual relief. An estimated 17 percent of farm and ranch boys still do. The frequency of sexual congress with animals is about 7 percent in cities and suburbs, where neither animals nor privacy are so easily come by.

With women direct massage of the glans clitoris is even rarer than direct massage of the glans penis is for men. Stimulating the clitoris by directly manipulating the female labial area, like manipulating the shaft of the penis, its analogue, is the most frequent practice. This is accomplished by using the fingers, the flat of the hand, water, or electric vibrators. Very few women insert penis substitutes into the vagina. When this is done, to add the stimulation of pressure in the vagina that is a part of coitus, it is accompanied by manipulation of the area around the clitoris. The idea that women masturbate vaginally is a male myth. The vagina is relatively insensitive. The clitoris is the female pleasure point.

A standard piece of bathroom equipment in most of the world is the bidet, which the woman uses for cleansing after using the toilet. This handy appliance was never adopted by our Puritan ancestors, who feared it might stimulate young women sexually, and so it never made its way to the British Isles or to North America. A bad mark for both. Not only is the bidet the ideal method for feminine cleanliness but it is also, as our ancestors feared it would be, highly sensually stimulating. A woman preparing for intercourse by washing her genitals in a bubbly bidet will be excited and eager for her partner when the cleaning rite is over.

When a woman hasn't a partner, the bubbler bidet provides an excellent method of complete sexual relief. The temperature and force of the bubbler can be preset. The woman straddles the bidet so that the fountain of water reaches the clitoral area, where the stimulation can quickly produce one or several orgasms.

The Danish hand-held "telephone" shower can also be used autoerotically by training its stream of water on the genitals.

Again, these showers, with their flexible hoses, are more often found elsewhere in the civilized world than here.

Some American women use the bathtub spigot autoerotically. The temperature and force of the water are regulated. Then the woman lies on her back in the tub, her hips at the spigot end, her legs in the air, so that the water from the tap runs over her genitals. Water at body temperature is soothing and for this reason many women prefer these water ways to other methods of autoerotic pleasure.

Different but Still Normal

The group masturbatory practices of adolescent boys could be labeled homosexual, and sometimes they lead to other homophile experiments. Kinscy found that by age furty-five, 50 percent of American men and 26 percent of the women had had some homosexual experience. Which hadn't kept most of them from engaging in heterosexual liaisons or from marrying.

"In view of the data," Kinsey wrote, "it is difficult to maintain the view that psychosexual reactions between individuals of the same sex are rare and therefore abnormal or unnatural, or that they constitute within themselves evidence of neuroses or even psychoses."

That was in 1948. A quarter of a century later, despite evidence corroborating Kinsey's, we still cling to our judgmental views on homophiles. Moralists condemn, jurists punish, psychiatrists try to cure, and parents and educators try to prevent. All this in spite of mounting evidence that homosexuals are not immoral, sick or abnormal.

In an effort to find out just how homosexuals differ from heterosexuals in other ways than sexual preference, research psychologist Dr. Evelyn Hooker, of the University of California at Los Angeles, selected thirty homosexual and thirty heterosexual men, matched according to age, education, and IQ. She gave each of them a questionnaire on his life history and a battery of psychological tests. Then she gave the results of the tests and the questionnaires to several psychiatrists and psychologists to analyze. So similar were the lives and psychological characteristics of the two groups that none of the experts could pick out the homosexuals.

Psychiatrist Dr. Martin Hoffman, of San Francisco's Center for Special Problems, has perhaps worked as closely with homosexuals as any therapist in the country. It is his belief that science has found no way to change the sexual preference of homophiles and that, therefore, "we are going to have to accept homosexuality as a valid way of life and remove the social and legal stigmas that are now attached to it."

As for preventing homosexuality by programming children into gender roles, Dr. Hoffman thinks we may have done too much of that. He believes that one possible reason there are only half as many female as male homosexuals is that we're much more tolerant of tomboy girls than of effeminate boys. It would seem that some youngsters reject their own sex simply because they find it impossible to live up to the rigid requirements society often sets for "masculine" men and "feminine" women.

The whole subject of homosexuality is clouded by mythology and misunderstanding. Bisexuals, for instance, are classified as homosexuals simply because they sometimes practice homosexuality. They also practice heterosexuality and might as accurately be called heterosexuals. Sexuality is, after all, a biological drive with no specific goals except satisfaction. Many anthropologists believe that in our past, before we discovered paternity and began directing sex toward reproduction, we were all bisexual.

Other cultures, particularly in the Middle East, bring up males to be bisexual. Where contact between the sexes is forbidden prior to marriage, and marriage is postponed for the male until he can afford the bride price, men are permitted to love each other before the wedding and expected to love their wives afterwards. Most of them do.

The lesson seems to be that homosexuality in our society is a sociological problem. We label, condemn, and ostracize those whose behavior is biologically sound and socially accepted in

other societies. We offer to "cure" the individuals we have stig-
matized. The cure doesn't work because it is applied in the wrong
area. It is society that is in need of corrective therapy, not the
individuals it has condemned and about which it knows almost
nothing.

Heterosexual myths about homosexuality are legion. The most
pervasive is the belief that homosexual men always act like
women and that homosexual women always act like men. In fact,
the most masculine men and the most feminine women can be,
and often are, homosexually oriented. While transvestites, who
like to dress in the clothing worn by the opposite sex, can be
either heterosexual or homosexual. Whatever else it may indicate,
a desire to cross-dress is not necessarily an indication of homosexuality.

Opposite-sex role playing has been dwindling on the homosexual scene for years, though the heterosexual society has failed
to notice. The last group of homosexuals to give up a burlesque
of heterosexual relationships were the Lesbians, who discarded
it some three or four years ago. As society in general has gone
toward unisex, so has the homosexual, and with as much relief
to be unburdened of the necessity for pretense.

More and more, experts are realizing that there is no such thing
as a "latent homosexual." Everyone who is alive has homosexual
desires and tendencies. There are times when each one of us feels
—and maybe acts—more "masculine" or "feminine" than might
be considered proper. These feelings and actions are as normal
in human beings as they are in the animal world.

We will know a great deal more about homosexuality when
the results of a recent study by the Institute for Sex Research,
founded by Dr. Alfred Kinsey, are made public. One of their findings, we already know, has indicated the effects of social disapproval on homosexuals.

From the age of eighteen to thirty homosexuals tend to worry
excessively about their homophile orientation and the disapproval of family and peers. For this reason they won't join gay
clubs or in other ways identify themselves as homosexuals. Sometimes their worries cause them to drop out of sexual activities
completely. Many males become impotent. Many females de-

velop vaginismus. Others try to hide their sexual preferences by condemning their own kind. This public belittling of homophiles is frequently led by heterosexuals who have difficulty admitting their own homosexual tendencies.

After the age of thirty both homosexuals and heterosexuals tend to give up the socially exacted codes, at least in private. Then homosexuals are quite willing to join gay societies and see what goes on. Hard-core heterosexuals such as construction workers—hardhats—and truck drivers often relax at this age too and indulge their own homosexual tendencies. Homosexuals know this and encourage the defectors. Truck drivers, for instance, can be propositioned on the highway—often successfully—with complicated codes of lighting signals. In addition, homosexuals will find that middle-aged "straights" frequently seek their advances. These are usually the fathers of growing families and have wives who have withdrawn sexually. The men feel that visiting a prostitute would be cheating but a homosexual encounter is all right as long as it is never known. These are often the same men who publicly ridicule and condemn homosexuals.

By the time the homosexual reaches the age of fifty he has come to terms with his sexual preference. Though heterosexual mythology assumes that it is tragic to be old and gay, the homosexual finds it quite otherwise. At fifty he gives up attempting to be something he is not—heterosexual. He usually has a lover who is his roommate, although not necessarily a sex partner. He moves easily in a gay society that he well understands and appreciates. And by this age he is able to have both homosexual and heterosexual friends, and mix with them without fear.

Most of the problems homosexuals face are imposed upon them by society. They have been persecuted unmercifully. Many of their sexual activities are against the law in most states so that they are constantly liable to prosecution as criminals and to victimization by blackmail. They are discriminated against in the job market, in housing, and in many public places, such as restaurants.

For these reasons many still feel that they must hide their homosexuality. In recent years, however, large numbers have joined together in homophile organizations that are not only social but also political. These organizations study the problems that homosexuals face and work to eliminate them. Fifteen years ago there were only fourteen such groups. Today there are more than two hundred, with vast numbers of members.

Most homosexuals of both sexes live very much like the rest of us. They fall in love, live together, call home if they are going to be late, give each other gifts, quarrel, make up, and make love. In part because society has been less condemnatory of Lesbians, and in part because they have been reared to be nestbuilders, homosexual women tend to live much like other women except that they live with each other.

Although there are some eighty-three bars catering to homosexual males in New York City, there are only two that cater to Lesbians. Although homosexual men are believed to outnumber practicing female homosexuals, the difference in numbers is not as great as this fact suggests. Men use their bars frequently for socializing and for meeting a variety of possible sexual partners. Once a partner is chosen, there is a more or less immediate sexual encounter, which may or may not develop into a relationship lasting over a period of time. A Lesbian, on the other hand, usually visits a bar only when unattached. Once she meets someone who appeals to her she and her prospective partner date several times, going to dinners and movies, before they become intimate. By this time they may be in love. Then they set up housekeeping together and often remain faithful to each other for long periods, sometimes for a lifetime.

Like heterosexuals, Lesbians are often jealous of their partners and demand fidelity. Male homosexuals are more permissive and frequently carry on a permanent relationship that includes numerous outside sexual contacts on both sides.

Lesbian households frequently contain children from the women's previous marriages. Lesbians are more likely than male homosexuals to marry when they are young in an attempt to "cure" themselves of homosexual tendencies, or simply because marriage is expected of them as women. Sometimes they marry just to have children.

A great many married women are bisexual, enjoying heterosexual acts with their husbands and homosexual relations with other women. Studies of these women show that the level of sexual activity with the female partner is usually much higher than with the male. So are the number of orgasms experienced per session. Many women who regularly have multiple orgasms in homosexual encounters have only one orgasm in heterosexual relations.

Kinsey accounts for this higher response in a homosexual situation by pointing out that "two individuals of the same sex are likely to understand the anatomy and physiological responses and psychology of their own sex better than they understand that of the opposite sex." Homophiles of both sexes often use this argument as proof that more intimacy exists in their relationships than in heterosexual pairing.

Kinsey also believes that the potential for bisexual response exists in all of us at birth but is carefully conditioned out in most of us so that we become exclusively heterosexual. Or sometimes exclusively homosexual. From that point of view heterosexuals are quite as "unnatural" as homosexuals.

Homosexuality is not a disease, as the Wolfenden Report made quite clear. It is a distinct way of life. Attempting to change this way of life to another way of life can be destructive of the entire personality. As we become more aware and more permissive of the sexual part of our own natures, we can better understand why some people focus sexually on members of the opposite sex, while others are attracted to members of the same sex.

4

Frogs Don't Make It

"Everybody was meant to be a prince or a princess," the late Eric Berne used to say, "but our parents turned us into frogs."

Our parents didn't mean to, of course. Their parents turned them into frogs, and their parents did the same to them, back through generations. The goal was never to create a frog. It was simply to make offspring socially acceptable, and society finds it a good deal easier to manage frogs than royalty. If the process is ever to change somebody is going to have to notice what has been happening and refuse to let the culture take away his royal birthright. It might as well be you.

Princes and princesses have more fun than frogs. They have more beautiful bodies and they enjoy them. They take pleasure from their senses and from the minutes and hours and days and nights allotted them. Since they were born equal they have no need to compete with each other and can devote themselves to fulfilling their very basic need for intimacy. And because they were born to the purple they feel worthy of giving and receiving love.

Intimacy as Inadequacy

People who have been rendered less than princes and princesses by their upbringing often feel unworthy of love and incapable of loving. Without meaning to, parents give them these ideas early in life. They do this with small remarks that damage the child's self-concept. And the damage can linger into adulthood, as Dr. Jane Vincent of North Dakota State University has discovered in a recent study of the effects on young adults of parents' negative judgments in childhood.

"Why are you always so selfish?" can make John or Jane feel too deficient in character to be loving or lovable. "Why do you do such stupid things?" can make the child feel intellectually deprived. "You're always so clumsy" renders him physically inferior. "You're impossible!" demolishes him.

The child is also affected adversely by suggestions that he doesn't meet the requirements of his gender role, or by slurs against either sex. "Don't be a sissy" not only leaves poor Johnny feeling that he is an inadequate male but also that sissies, meaning girls, are inadequate people who wouldn't be worthy of his love even if he were man enough to be worthy of theirs. "You're as awkward as a man," can have much the same effect on Jane.

It's the female sex that is most often downgraded, with pernicious effects on the self-image of little girls, on little boys' ideas of little girls, and on their adult relationships. Parents aren't the only ones responsible for this calumny. Educators, advertisers, and the mass media constantly portray women as witless incompetents, slightly inferior to dogs as pets, not quite up to machines as helpers.

Learning to read from a basic reading program adopted by schools throughout the country, boys and girls alike learn that when a boy and a girl try to skate the boy is capable of mastering the art. The girl isn't. She falls down and quits. "She is just like a girl," says the boy. "She gives up."

On television, women are normally presented either as sex objects or as helpmates concerned with nothing more important than easy-to-cook meals, the latest gossip, or the whiteness of the wash. Women have traditionally been encouraged to wait for Prince Charming to come along. Wait, they are told, for him to bring love into your life. Wait for children to fulfill you. Wait for grandchildren to give meaning to your final years. All you have to do to make it all come true is use the right mouthwash and deodorant, perfume and shampoo. Or become a blonde and have more fun. Men will flock to these lures and bring you happiness.

"We are raising a nation of hysteric-dependent women," warns Santa Monica sex counselor Dr. Alex Runciman, who holds the media responsible in large part.

Hysteric-dependent women aren't happy women, or even whole people. Waiting for others to make life worth living just doesn't get the job done. Yet that is what women are taught to do from the moment they learn, while learning to read, that giving up and not trying is the way to be just like a girl.

Men in our culture are also short-changed. The little boy learning to read learns that if he can't master skating and outdo a girl, he is less than a male. He must always be strong, able, aggressive, and successfully competitive. In our society he is allowed no outlets for the natural feminine side of his nature. Trying to play this circumscribed and demanding male role cuts years off his life.

Much to the horror of their elders, young people have been revolting against these sexual stereotypes. The men have adopted long hair and the women wear jeans. It's impossible to tell the boys from the girls, complains the shocked Establishment.

But the kids know the difference. As author Faubion Bowers has noted, "As more femininity is released by men, the more masculinely they make out. Take any average night in New York City and you'll see more so-called hippie types with their chicks than hardhats with their womenfolk. The hardhats regularly attend their all-man hangouts, and when they are home, they often polish their cars when they should be stroking their women."

Never having been allowed to develop any of their caring qualities, which have been labeled feminine, the typical male in our society has never learned how to stroke a woman, or to be stroked by her. He has never had permission from society to admit his need for intimacy, so it has been pushed down into his subconscious—where eventually it manifests itself as bleeding ulcers or atherosclerosis.

Silence and Secrecy

Social approval of our sexuality is important if we are to develop into sexually healthy adults. We learn as children through the approval and disapproval of our behavior by the significant adults in our lives. When behavior is punished we learn that it is shameful. We learn the same thing when it is ignored by adults who are silently upset by it.

This is what happens today when children explore their own sexual natures and the bodies of their playmates. Modern American parents no longer punish but they send silent signals of dismay as they carefully ignore the offending behavior. And they don't give permission to the learning child to explore his genitals and sexual feelings with the same healthy curiosity he expends on the rest of his environment. Nobody tells him his genitals are "pretty" or "handsome" or asks if he finds his sexual play pleasurable.

The adolescent with his sexually maturing body is naturally curious about his imminent sex role, but he is barred from almost every legal means of satisfying his curiosity. Even movies portraying the sexual activities of his own generation are restricted to "Adults Only." As are any legitimate movies that treat sex frankly, and sometimes honestly and artistically as well. Nor can he freely satisfy his curiosity in shops selling pornographic reading material or in movie houses specializing in the portrayal of sexual activity. Allowing him access to these, it is assumed, would warp his character.

Studies show that this does not happen. In Denmark, which recently legalized pornography of all kinds, there has been a marked and continuing diminution of sexual crime. In America, researchers have found that rapists and child molesters actually received *less* exposure to pornography during adolescence than did normal heterosexual adults. One study conducted by Dr. Michael J. Goldstein, of the University of California at Los Angeles, and Harold S. Kant, director of California's Legal and Behavioral Institute, compared 60 men convicted of, or charged with, sex offenses, with 52 regular patrons of pornography shops, and 63 solid citizen controls.

What the researchers found was that all groups of sexual deviates shared one common characteristic—"they had little exposure to erotica when they were adolescents." The normal adults in the sample reported more experience with pornography both as teenagers and as adults than did the sex offenders. There was no evidence that pornography contributed in any way to sex crimes.

The researchers concluded that "a reasonable exposure to erotica, particularly during adolescence, reflects a high degree of sexual interest and curiosity that correlates with adult patterns of acceptable heterosexual interest and practice."

Pornography, it seems, is an important and necessary part of sexual education. Yet we make youngsters get it on their own from underground purveyors whose interest is not in teaching but in turning a buck. For profit they cater to the tastes of the sexually maladjusted.

In doing so they perform a social service by providing a safety valve for those whose bizarre sexual behavior might otherwise be socially disruptive. But they certainly provide an inferior educational service for our adolescents and for the many normal, heterosexual adults who increasingly turn to pornography not only as a sexual stimulant but in an attempt to fill in the gaps in their own inadequate sexual education.

Obviously what we need is not a crackdown on pornography but an upgrading of the product to fulfill its educational function.

Recently, the Report of the Commission on Pornography and Obscenity, compiled by a group of social scientists at the request of the President—and at a cost to the taxpayers of two million dollars—suggested that the laws governing obscenity were obsolete and that we should follow the Danes in making pornography legal, at least for adults. These findings of the experts have dropped quietly into limbo, because they don't happen to jibe with our unscientific prejudices—prejudices that have caused us to neglect the sexual education of our youngsters in other and even more hurtful ways.

Romance versus Reality

We give our young people all sorts of help in choosing and preparing for a career but none at all in preparing for marriage and choosing a mate. Here we let the movies and television do the educating. They teach that love is something that "happens" to you. When it happens it brings happiness. And changes sex from something bad to something good.

Young people buy these Hollywood lessons. Girls in particular confuse sexual desire with love. Having been taught that only bad girls experience the former they decide that their own feelings must be inspired by the latter. The result is a teenage marriage, with its poor chance of survival, or pregnancy, or both. Forty-two percent of all brides under twenty are pregnant, a recent government survey disclosed. And fourteen percent of all births are illegitimate.

Let a Hollywood-inspired teenage girl in a home for unwed mothers explain why she doesn't want to take the Pill: "That's for promiscuous girls. I'm not promiscuous. I was in love. I wouldn't have done it if I wasn't in love. Taking the Pill every day would make me feel I was going to be bad and I don't want to be. Love should be unexpected. Not something you prepare for. That takes away all the romance."

Obviously such garbled notions of love and sex don't keep young people from expressing their sexuality, often with tragic results. But we condone and even promote these ideas as if they had proved helpful. And we reinforce them by restricting the dispensation of contraceptive information and devices and making abortion, in most states, a criminal offense.

These measures work against the poor. Sexual expression, like clipping coupons, is a privilege reserved for the affluent. Thirty percent of brides from families earning less than $3,000 a year go to the altar pregnant. Only eight percent from families with incomes of over $10,000 are expecting when married.

The difference is not in chastity but in economics, and the ability to cope that education brings with it. The affluent know where birth control devices and abortions can be procured, and are able to cross state lines and national borders to avail themselves of these pregnancy preventives. The poor stay home and have babies, or criminal or do-it-yourself abortions.

The underground abortion racket is the third biggest criminal racket in the United States, exceeded only by gambling and prostitution. Its estimated yearly death toll is equal to the annual casualties in the Vietnam war. More than half these murdered women are wives and mothers who leave behind small children who still need their care. The other half are young women who, without trial, received the death sentence for the double crime of being sexually active and poor in a society that believes the former is a sin for women and the latter a sin for everyone.

Love as Mystery

Laws aren't needed to force young people to marry or to bear children. Surveys show that most young people want to do both. And eventually most of them do. The problem for the future, if society wishes to prevent overpopulation and still preserve marriage, will be to give marriage a validity other than the rearing of children.

Certainly the fulfillment of the human's basic need for intimacy is a valid reason for marriage. But intimacy is not furthered by laws that make the bearing of unwanted children mandatory. Neither are these laws helpful in solving the problem of over-population.

Indeed, while professing to believe in marriage, society does little to bolster it and much to hamper it. In our schools young-sters learn more about the moon than about marriage. Though the social scientists have been studying it for years, love is still the great mystery. Nobody tries to explain it to the student as they explain the atom and its nucleus.

Why are young people not introduced to the psychology of interpersonal relationships in high school? No subject could be more meaningful. Surely youngsters developing sexually would be better off knowing that though sex and love often coexist, they are not the same thing. Sex is undiscriminating. Love wants a particular person.

And why one person rather than another? According to Theo-dor Reik, one of many psychologists with a theory about this most puzzling phenomenon, we leap into love with someone who has qualities we wish we had and feel we lack. How hard we fall depends on how despairingly inadequate we feel. We start by envying the other person the qualities we desire. We may even hate him for possessing them. Then we understand that by loving him we can possess both the person and the desired qualities.

All this happens below the level of consciousness. We are aware only that we are fascinated by this particular person. Lov-ing him, we identify with him. He becomes not only part of the self, but the better part of the self, because he brings the self closer to the dreamed-of ideal. We can give everything to the beloved because the giving adds rather than takes away from the new self into which the loved one has been incorporated.

But the subconscious hostile emotions that preceded love are still there beneath the surface and they flare up now and then in quarrels and even violence. Those who don't understand that "love and hate are two horns on the same goat," as the British say, may doubt their love when hostility emerges. But hostility and love *do* exist together. It is not hostility, which is often displaced self-hatred, but indifference to the loved one that spells the death of love, according to Reik.

Another of his theories is that self-hatred is responsible for jealousy. You are jealous for the same reason you fall in love— because of a feeling of inadequacy. The feeling was there before you fell in love and has less to do with whether or not your loved one loves you than whether or not you love yourself. When you're feeling confident, you're not jealous. When you feel inferior to all the others he might have loved, or might be tempted to love, then jealousy torments you.

Unfortunately such helpful and probing analyses of love relationships are not part of a teenager's education. Lacking such guidance, young people confuse sexual desire with love and get married to justify sexual activity, or for a variety of other reasons that have nothing to do with cherishing one another. For some reason society considers this better than allowing them alternatives that would be more suitable both to their sexual maturity and their psychological immaturity. Two out of every three teenage marriages end in annulment, separation, or divorce.

For those who postpone marriage past the teenage years, the dissolution rate falls to one in four marriages and the happiness in intact marriages rises, surveys show. But not too much. A majority of couples married twenty years say they are not happy together, and increasing numbers of them are getting divorces instead of celebrating silver anniversaries.

Though divorce should be considered a boon, with the second chance it offers for happiness, the divorced are still outcasts in our couples society. So are the singles, for that matter. Both are discriminated against socially, psychologically, and even financially.

This is particularly true in their search for new mates, or even just dates. Recently investigators on the West coast have been collecting data on the way many singles organizations, old-fashioned matchmakers, and new-fangled computer dating services fleece their customers. There have been reports of thefts and attempted rapes at singles club parties, of money paid for mating and dating services never rendered, of mismatching even by services who claim to screen members, and of gigolos being hired as dates for women clients.

The investigators found that dating services that charge hundreds of dollars are no more trustworthy than those that charge five or fifteen. Some of the latter have been around since computer dating began and, although honest, they have failed to keep up with the sophistication of their clients. They are used by married people looking for affairs, by fortune hunters, and occasionally by swingers searching for a third or a fourth.

For some reason the psychologists and sociologists who first started computer dating, and heralded it as a new, scientific way to pick a mate, have deserted the field, despite a really desperate need for some method that will bring compatible single and divorced people together. This need has now reached the attention of psychiatrists and other therapists who find many of the lonely people who come to them for help would benefit more from companionship than counseling. Perhaps from their concern will come new ways to solve the problem.

Despite the difficulties of meeting and mating in our impersonal, urban world, people manage. They marry and remarry, always with hope that love will grow and flower and forever fill their deep need for intimacy. And sometimes this happens, though our modern world isn't really set up to nourish such a delicate plant as love.

The energetic hours of the day are invariably reserved for work, not love and play. And work is separated from home, sometimes by several commuting hours. So the triumphs and emergencies of both career and family are shared not with the intimate partner but with coworkers, or neighbors, or no one.

Husbands are overnight guests in the homes of their wives. Wives are strangers in the offices of their husbands. And when their children are born, the parents are separated by the doors of the maternity ward and the regulations of the hospital.

These facts of life place a tremendous burden on the marital relationship. Husbands buckle and break under their unrelenting economic burden. Wives grow lonely and frustrated, isolated with their children. In the fifty-year life expectancy of modern marriage, both partners can change. Society makes it easier for them to grow apart than together.

Love has a better chance when intimate partners understand the hazards their love faces in today's world. Then they can build their relationship on realistic expectations. Rather than blaming themselves or each other when the relationship flounders, they can assess their troubles rationally and look for solutions that take account of the cultural obstacles that lie in the path of intimacy.

Love between frogs has reason to be blind. Princes and princesses love with their eyes wide open, knowing it is a precious kingdom over which they watch.

5

Body Barriers to Intimacy

Since intimacy is communication in which you use your body, its care is important. Any physical distress that threatens to interfere with intimate relations should receive prompt attention. Too often such private matters are treated, instead, with neglect. Not only are lay people shy about taking sexual troubles to a physician, but some physicians are ill-equipped to handle these problems.

It is only in the past few years that medical schools generally have been teaching students about sex, and as yet the instruction is far from adequate. Most medical texts give the subject only passing mention or ignore it completely. One general text discusses at length seven possible impairments of the function of walking but avoids entirely any mention of the possibility of sexual malfunction.

Fortunately the picture is changing. Medical students have not been immune to the sexual revolution, and medical schools are no longer run like monasteries. Increasingly, students marry and start families while they are still in school. Improved instruction and their own experience combine to make them well aware of the importance of sex in every phase of life, and sympathetic and informed when they encounter sexual problems in their practices.

Chances are your physician is one who understands the importance of sex to physical well-being. If you feel he doesn't un-

derstand your problem, ask him to recommend a consultant.
Reputable doctors are quite willing to do this. If he refuses, then
change doctors. Your county or state medical society can provide
names of other physicians.

When You Are Young

Because youth is the time of greatest sexual activity it is also
the time when sexual problems most frequently reveal themselves. Unfortunately, young people are often more reluctant
than their elders to take their difficulties to a doctor. So the problems grow worse and, if untreated, may haunt a lifetime. Many
could be prevented by early and regular medical checkups, including pelvic examinations.

A recent test program involving 1.7 million women throughout
the country established the fact that cervical cancer can, and
does, occur in teenage girls. The U.S. Public Health Service, who
conducted the program with the American Academy of General
Practice, recommends that women start having annual Papanicolaou (Pap) smear tests at age 16 and continue throughout
their lives.

Since cervical cancer is curable when detected in its early
stages, regular examinations will prevent cancer spread, not only
of the cervix but also of the breast. The doctor will examine the
breasts for lumps and teach the patient to do so too, preferably
every month.

Self-examination is quickly and easily done. Use the right hand
to examine the left breast. With your hand push the breast firmly
against the chest and feel for lumps within the tissue. Then lean
forward and let the breast fall into your hand, cupped to fit
around it. Feel for lumps again. Repeat on the opposite side, using the left hand to examine the right breast.

A lump should immediately be reported to your doctor, even

though it's much more likely to be benign than malignant. Benign tumors sometimes disappear by themselves or they can be removed by local surgical excision that leaves only a small scar. The most modern treatment for malignant tumors is also excision, combined with radiation, which leaves the breast intact. But this method can only be used if the malignancy is found early. This fact in itself should motivate self-examination and regular visits to the physician.

These visits will accustom the woman to the examination of her genitals and to the penetration of her vagina by the physician's fingers. If penetration is difficult or impossible, the physician will be able to treat the trouble before it becomes a sexual problem, affecting both the woman and her intimate partner.

One obstacle to vaginal access is a tough and inelastic hymen. The hymen is a membrane that partially closes the vaginal opening. Usually it is thin and easily stretched or torn with little or no pain. Though the presence of the hymen used to be considered the sign of a virgin, today's active, athletic young women may well lose theirs without losing their virginity.

If, on the other hand, the hymen is firm and obstructive it can impede not only the doctor's examination but also later sexual union. The doctor may snip the membrane, which can be done with only surface anesthesia. Or he may show the patient how to stretch the hymen.

This can be done with a finger lubricated with surgical jelly. Insert the finger slowly for a few minutes each day. When it can be inserted to its full length, begin to move it backward and from side to side. Do this until it is possible to insert two fingers without discomfort.

The advantage of self-dilation of the vaginal opening is that this acquaints the woman with her vagina and its ability to expand. It also stretches and relaxes the muscles at the entrance to the vagina.

If the woman has a condition called vaginismus, dilation will be a larger, longer project. Vaginismus consists of involuntary spasms of the muscles at the mouth of the vagina whenever entrance to this opening is attempted. Women often don't realize that they exhibit this reaction but the examining physician can recognize it, for it will occur when he tries to make a pelvic examination.

If the condition goes undetected until intercourse is attempted, it can make sexual union painful for both partners, or completely impossible. Marriages have gone unconsummated for years while couples waited for vaginismus to clear up of its own accord. Very often by the time they ask for help, the female partner's disability has caused potency problems in the male and strained the relationship to the breaking point.

Vaginismus is a psychosomatic ailment. It can be caused by too many childhood enemas, overly strict religious upbringing, rape, criminal abortion, or repeated episodes of painful coitus. The most successful treatment consists of slow dilation of the vaginal opening with Hegar dilators. These are phallus-shaped plastic tubes that come in graduated sizes. Lubricated with surgical jelly, the smallest is inserted gently and with an uninterrupted motion into the vagina. For a moment or two it may cause discomfort. Nevertheless, it should be allowed to remain in place for several minutes.

The following day, or even sooner, the next size dilator is introduced into the vagina. Since the size changes are gradual pain is eliminated and discomfort kept to a minimum. If dilation is practiced every day, the largest sizes should be comfortably inserted within a week and the worst of the spasms eliminated.

When this point has been reached the dilator should be left in place for several hours every night. And for the first month or six weeks preliminary dilation of the vaginal opening may be necessary before intercourse. Treatment of the psychological reason for the physical difficulty may also be advisable.

Physical Barriers to Intercourse

Painful intercourse (dyspareunia), one of the causes of vaginismus, can itself have many causes. A common one is insufficient vaginal lubrication. With sexual excitement the lining of the vagina exudes or "sweats" moisture. This reaction is the equivalent of an erection in a man. It is not a sign (as some marriage manuals say it is) that the woman is ready for penetration and orgasm. It is a sign that she is psychologically interested in this sexual encounter and that this growing interest is beginning to prepare her body for sexual union.

If she isn't interested there is no moisture, and coitus may be painful for both partners. There are many reasons for a lack of sexual excitement and therefore of vaginal lubrication. The woman who has been strictly brought up may not have learned to think or feel sexually. She may believe it is wrong to do so. Or she may be afraid of intercourse or of pregnancy.

Often her uninformed or inexperienced partner doesn't realize that she must be prepared both psychologically and physically for coitus. Instead, he enters when *he* is ready, trusting to penile thrusting to excite his partner. Under these circumstances it is more apt to cause them both pain.

Occasionally sexual disinterest, resulting in lack of lubrication, is caused by birth control pills. The Pill prevents pregnancy by changing the hormonal balance in the body. Most women seem to adjust to the change with no disturbance of their sexual drive. In some the effect of the Pill is actually to increase sexual interest. In others, however, the Pill acts to suppress excitement.

Either effect is reversible if the woman is taken off the Pill and given another form of contraception for a few months. Or the doctor may simply change pills, giving her one with a different concentration of hormones, or one which delivers the hormones in sequence.

Sometimes pain during coitus is caused by tags of tissue left when the hymen was broken. Nearly every woman has some part of her hymen left, regardless of age or the number of children she has borne. If this tissue becomes irritated or infected it can cause extreme discomfort. Surgery so simple it can be done in a doctor's office remedies the situation. Sometimes women request that a new hymen be constructed from the remaining tissue. In this way they become "virgins" again.

The vagina is a remarkable self-cleaning orifice with the ability to protect itself against infection. Protection comes from a strongly acid environment in which most bacteria and other disease invaders can't live. They can acquire a stronghold, however, during menstruation, when the level of vaginal acidity falls, or if the acidity is disturbed in other ways.

Many women disturb the acid level constantly by douching, in an effort to keep the vagina clean and odorless. The vagina keeps itself clean and odorless. Careful washing of the exterior genital area is all that is needed, even after menstruation and intercourse. This can be tested by cleaning the vulval area carefully while bathing and then inserting a finger in the vagina. The finger will have absolutely no odor.

Odors build up in the exterior genitals from lack of cleanliness and can best be eliminated with *mild* soap and water. Most of our soaps are much too harsh. Ask your doctor to recommend a soap and use it for your entire body. The much advertised "feminine hygiene" sprays and powders are no substitute for soap and water and can be irritating to genital tissues.

Though too much cleansing of the vagina can prepare the way for bacterial infections and consequent painful intercourse, insufficient cleansing of the external genitals can also cause infection and dyspareunia. This frequently happens when smegma builds up beneath the clitoral prepuce, causing irritation and burning when this foreskin is moved as the penis enters the vagina. Rolling the foreskin back and cleansing the surface regularly prevents the trouble and eliminates a most important cause of genital odor. Occasionally adhesions anchor the foreskin to the clitoris, making its movement difficult and painful. Then a physician's help may be needed.

Itching, burning, and aching in the vagina can be caused by bacterial, fungus, or trichomonal invasions of the canal, which produce an annoying and uncomfortable discharge. A physician can determine which is to blame and treat the condition. Many women put up with a discharge from the vagina, or try to treat it with home remedies. Since effective treatment varies with the agent causing the infection, it must be prescribed by a physician. Treatment, of course, is easier, quicker, and more successful the sooner the problem is brought to his attention.

If the infection comes from fecal matter that has contaminated the genitals the physician can't, of course, keep it from recurring. Cleanliness is the best prevention. Underclothing should be changed often and the anus cleaned carefully after evacuation. No object that has first been introduced into the anus should be placed in the vagina without thorough cleansing.

When trichomonads are the vaginal invaders both intimate partners should be treated, even though the female may be the only one experiencing any symptoms. Men harbor the trichomonad parasites, often in the prostate gland, seminal vesicles, or bladder, and can reinfect the partner if the contamination is not eliminated.

Women aren't the only ones who suffer from painful intercourse. It can happen to men too. Both can develop allergic reactions to contraceptive foams, rubber appliances, or douching compounds used by the female. Some men are allergic to the acid climate of the vagina.

Unless uncircumcised men wash carefully under the foreskin of the penile glans, smegma can build up, causing chronic irritation. Sometimes the foreskin can't be retracted over the glans because of adhesions or a constriction of the prepuce orifice. Then infection is difficult to prevent and pain may accompany erection as the engorged glans presses against its confining cover. Circumcision provides permanent relief.

Just because circumcision is indicated for the relief of some pathological conditions does not mean that our present practice of circumcising almost all male babies is necessary or advisable. It is frequently recommended as a means of avoiding cancer, believed to be transmitted through the smegma beneath the foreskin. In fact, neither uncircumcised males nor their wives have a higher incidence of cancer than the rest of the population, nor do they contract more venereal disease. The prepuce that covers the penile glans is nature's way of protecting this extremely sensitive organ. It would seem meddlesome to remove this protection except for serious medical causes. Modern cleanliness has eliminated most of the conditions that once convinced physicians routine circumcision was desirable.

Sexual stimulation can become painful for males if it is prolonged without orgasmic relief. Younger men often experience an aching in the testicles and perineum—the space between the testicles and anus—under these conditions. The pain can be relieved through ejaculation, and should be. Otherwise the swollen and painful condition could become chronic. This inflammation is called prostatitis. Possibly a third of all adult men under forty and two thirds of males over that age suffer from it to some degree.

Much prostate trouble results from neglect of the prostate, the small gland that manufactures an important part of the fluid that the male ejaculates. Walnut-sized, the prostate stands sentinel over the urethra at the entrance to the bladder. A distended bladder reduces circulation to the gland. Men who regularly delay going to the bathroom are simply asking for prostate trouble. Men who constantly ride horses, trucks, or motorcycles also punish their prostate glands unduly. Chronic prostatitis can lead to enlargement of the gland, which then interferes with urination and ejaculation.

Sometimes men experience a sudden stabbing pain in the rectum for which no cause can be found. Usually this pain will come and go intermittently over a three- or four-day period. Each episode of pain is intense and very brief—twenty to thirty seconds. Dr. Walter Alvarez postulates that the pain is caused by a clot in a small blood vessel of the prostate. The final result is the formation of a small stone within the gland. This acts as an irritant and increases the degree of prostatitis. Rectal massage is helpful, as is sexual activity maintained on a regular basis. Every annual physical should include a rectal examination of the prostate.

Painful intercourse is sometimes the result of permanent damage to the penis, inflicted on the erect organ by a sudden blow, bending, or pressure. Hemorrhage in the shaft can cause adhesions and scars, with attendant tenderness and pain, and sometimes produce a change in angulation. Any pain during or after ejaculation, including burning and itching, should receive prompt medical attention. The cause may be infection in the bladder, prostate, or seminal vesicles. And the infection may be gonorrhea, which, despite the old saying, is a good deal worse than a bad cold.

Well Known Venereal Diseases

The gonococcus micro-organism that causes gonorrhea usually attacks the urethra of the male and the urethra, vagina and cervix of the female. It can also invade the rectum, as a result of anal intercourse. Or it can spread there from the genitals. Occasionally it spreads to other parts of the body as well.

It is always acquired through sexual contact. Dirty drinking glasses, towels, or toilet seats are not to blame. Neither is muscular strain—popular opinion notwithstanding. The gonococcus cannot survive outside the warm, moist environment of mucous membranes.

Symptoms of gonorrhea appear two days to a week after infection. Besides a burning sensation when urinating or ejaculating, the genitals may become red and swollen. And there is always a discharge. At first this is watery, but it becomes thicker in the following day or two. It is creamy and greenish-yellow in color.

If left untreated, the infection can spread throughout the urinary tract, causing pain and swelling. It can enter the bloodstream and affect the whole body, producing such complications as arthritis, inflammation of the eye, skin eruptions, and involvement of the brain and the valves of the heart.

Antibiotics cure the disease, though not as swiftly or dramatically as they did short years ago. Drug-resistant strains of the bacteria develop, demanding ever new and stronger defenses. This is one reason that our wonder drugs have not eliminated gonorrhea, as it was once supposed they would. Instead, the frequency of the contagion is increasing throughout the world.

Oral antibiotics, taken before or after sexual exposure, prevent venereal disease and could perhaps wipe it out, at least in the United States. But even when this protection is given men in the armed forces there is a protest of moral indignation. The prevention of venereal infection is decried as the encouragement of sin. Until the public becomes less sin-conscious and more health-conscious, venereal disease will be tolerated, as bubonic plague, smallpox, and other less "wicked" scourges have not been.

Gonorrhea is one of man's oldest diseases. It is described in early Chinese writings and in the Bible. Some medical historians think that the Hebrew rite of circumcision may have originated as a means of relief for one of the complications of gonorrhea—balanitis—an inflammation of the glans penis.

Syphilis is a relatively new threat to human health. It grew to epidemic proportions in Europe shortly after Columbus came back from discovering America. Whether or not he also discovered the disease is still a debated question. At any rate he was blamed for it, then and now, and for the sexual restrictions that syphilis imposed on European sexual behavior, once the venereal transmission of the disease was understood. Says Gordon Roberts, of San Francisco, "Columbus didn't just discover America. He also discovered fidelity."

The terrifying new disease spread swiftly throughout Europe, identified in each country by the name of another. It was "the French disease" in England, "the Spanish disease" in France. Once its method of transmission became known, public baths and other places where the sexes commingled were closed. The Church's hitherto blinked-at commandments of celibacy or fidelity to an uninfected partner became life-saving measures, widely adopted and preached. Fidelity became the law. And such words as "adultery" took on new meaning.

These measures may have slowed, but they certainly didn't halt, the spread of syphilis. It is doubtful if any person of European heritage alive today doesn't have a few syphilitic ancestors. This inheritance, in fact, gives a measure of protection that less "civilized" people don't have.

The first sign of syphilis is the chancre, or sore, that develops at the place where the spirochete that causes the disease was transferred from one person to another. Chancres most frequently appear on the genitals, because the infecting organism can only exist in a warm, moist place. It is agile, but fragile. Nevertheless, when conditions are right, it can transfer itself to other places than the genitals, such as the mouth or lips, for instance.

The chancre is usually a small, red, angry-appearing pimple that causes no pain and heals quickly. However, it contains the infecting organism, *Treponema pallidum,* that can transmit the disease to another person. Swollen glands usually develop with the chancre and are more painful than the lesion itself.

When the chancre heals the victim of syphilis may feel that he has nothing to worry about. For two to six months he has no symptoms, nor does he transmit the disease. Indeed, many women are infected without knowing it since their painless chancres are deep within the vagina where they cannot be seen.

Secondary syphilis, which develops at the end of the initial quiet period, presents very noticeable symptoms. There are skin eruptions and wartlike lesions in the body folds. Other lesions appear in the mouth, vulva, and anus. But the disease is, as it was once called, "the great imitator." The troubles can be diagnosed as many different things.

Because of the great number of open sores, syphilis is especially contagious in its secondary stage. The quiet stage after that may last for twenty or thirty years, during which the invading spirochetes silently and slowly destroy brain tissues and the central nervous system.

Less Known Venereal Diseases

Gonorrhea and syphilis are not the only venereal diseases. Chancroid is also a hazard. This disease begins with a chancre that looks somewhat like the chancre of syphilis and occurs twelve to thirty-six hours after sexual contact. The sore can be less than an inch in size or destructive of large areas of skin. Because it is painful, as syphilitic chancres are not, it is more readily taken to physicians. The cure is simple and quick. A doctor usually has the trouble under control within eight days.

Lymphogranuloma venereum is not so easily cured at present. It makes its first appearance a few days after sexual contact with an infected person. A small blister appears on the penis, vulva, vaginal walls, or cervix. The blister bursts, leaving a shallow grayish ulcer surrounded by reddened skin. Sometimes these lesions can be found in the urethra, the anus, or, following oral contact, on the tongue.

A week or two after the initial symptoms, the local lymph glands are infected. They swell, grow painful, and break down with inflammation and pus. Chills, sweats, fever, prostration, nausea, vomiting, headache, and stiffness of the neck develop during this secondary stage. If untreated, lymphogranuloma venereum can break down the tissues between the rectum, vagina, and bladder, leading to death from sepsis.

Not properly a venereal disease, since in many cases it seems not to be transmitted through sexual intercourse, granuloma inguinale is still a genital hazard. It is characterized by lesions that grow and spread, replacing healthy tissue with a granulation that is red, moist, and fetid. The infection may start on the face, neck, groin, or anus, but usually begins on the penis or labia and spreads through the genitals. Despite this location, the sexual partner rarely becomes infected. The disease can be cured with antibiotics within a period of one or two weeks.

There was a time when men with warts on their penises considered themselves more attractive sexual partners because of the size that the warts added to their sexual organs. Recent studies have shown that the warts, officially known as condyloma acuminata, are caused by a virus which can cause cervical cancer in the female. The warts are easily removed, and should be. No man who has them should indulge in sexual intercourse until he has undergone successful treatment for the condition. And no woman who values her health should allow a man with venereal warts to enter her vagina.

Condoms are an excellent protection against venereal disease. So is soap and water, or an antiseptic douche, used immediately after intercourse. When in doubt don't take chances. And don't hesitate to consult your doctor about sexual problems. They are no more shameful than any other physical troubles.

Venereal disease flourishes when it is considered a punishment for sin rather than a physical infection. Every city has venereal disease clinics where detection and treatment are available free or for a nominal sum. So neither poverty nor prudery should keep you from seeking help if you suspect you may have acquired a venereal infection.

When You Are Mature

There was a time when repeated childbearing stretched a woman's vagina, robbing her and her partner of full sexual pleasure. Sometimes, too, vaginal tears, unrepaired after delivery, left scars that made intercourse painful for the female.

Today's obstetricians customarily prevent and correct any damage to the vagina that occurs during childbirth so that the woman comes through the experience, or several birth experiences, physically unchanged. If any problems remain, it is essential to arrange for them to be fixed rather than to be stoically endured. Occasionally poor obstetrical care, or a mismanaged criminal abortion, can actually damage the sexual organs, producing pain or sexual anesthesia. A competent physician can ordinarily find and rectify the trouble.

Sometimes pelvic pain during coital thrusting is caused by damage to the ligaments that support the uterus. With deep penetration the woman feels as if the penis were hitting something tender. A poorly supported womb may also be responsible for nagging backache and pelvic heaviness. The damaged ligaments can be repaired with surgery.

Anything that interferes with the flexibility of a woman's internal pelvic organs can produce painful reactions during intercourse. Adhesions and fibrosis, the growth of abnormal tissue within the pelvis, can render pelvic organs stationary and vulnerable to painful stress from sexual excitement or coital activity.

One cause of fibrosis is endometriosis, in which implants of tissue, resembling that which lines the uterus, spread through the pelvis, producing adhesions and irritation. The tissue invasion must often be corrected surgically.

Occasionally after hysterectomy, the surgical removal of the womb, pain during intercourse can develop at the site of the vaginal scar. This happens if the inflexible scar is pulled into the depth of the vagina, where it is struck by the end of the penis, instead of remaining on the upper vaginal wall. More often, sexual difficulties after hysterectomy are the result of fears and old wives' tales. Particularly if the ovaries have been removed along with the womb, both the woman and her husband may decide that her sexual life is over.

Actually, it should be improved after the operation has eliminated a cause of ill-health. Even if the ovaries have been removed, the hormones they once produced can be taken orally. They will have the same effect on a woman's system as hormones created internally.

Hormone replacement is also given after menopause to make up for any lessening of female sex steroids suffered as the ovaries slow production. This replacement doesn't seem necessary to stimulate sexual desire, which continues in any case. But it does prevent the thinning of vaginal walls that sometimes makes intercourse painful for older women. When lack of hormones, or of sexual activity, has resulted in vaginal atrophy, the process can be reversed with hormone pills or injections and hormonal vaginal creams or suppositories.

Drugs and disease can cause sexual disinterest and incapacity. Alcohol notoriously increases sexual desire and decreases sexual ability. Addictive drugs rob the addict even of desire. Reserpine used for the relief of hypertension can cause impotence, as can other drugs sometimes prescribed for physical disabilities. When a loss of sexual interest or capacity is a side effect of your medication don't hesitate to mention it to your physician. He may be able to change treatment so that sexual function isn't disturbed.

One disease that seems to predispose to impotence in the male and sexual indifference in the female is diabetes mellitus. This is a metabolic malfunctioning characterized by too much sugar in the blood and too little nutrition of bodily tissues, including the nerves. It is an extremely common disease, with four million known cases in the United States and possibly as many undiagnosed.

Classic symptoms include overweight and continuous hunger, thirst, and urinary urgency. A blood sugar test taken over a period of five hours will determine whether or not you have diabetes. In most instances the trouble can be controlled through diet. And control will eliminate the physical causes of sexual incapacity. It won't, of course, remove the psychological fear of performance that the male may have acquired from his diabetic experience with erective failure.

The mind is often responsible, as well, for the impotence that sometimes follows prostatectomy, or that occurs with aging. The man has been told, and has told himself, that the operation, or the accumulation of birthdays, will affect his sexual performance. So he talks himself into nonperformance. The aging man does this the minute he finds his sexual responses slowing down.

They may slow down with age, just as his walking gait does, but that's no reason he should stop either activity. Sexual expression in both males and females can continue into the eighties and beyond if it has been a regular part of their lives and if they don't develop psychological blocks.

Even heart trouble no longer calls inevitably for sexual retirement. In a recent study Herman Hellerstein and Ernest Friedman, of Case Western Reserve University School of Medicine in Ohio, found that during sexual intercourse the heart rate rose no higher than in many other daily activities. And the acceleration lasted only for ten or fifteen seconds.

Subjects used in the study had either suffered coronaries or had a tendency to heart disease. Portable tape recorders automatically made electrocardiograms of each man's activities through two days and nights. Concluded the researchers: "Over 80 percent of men who have had a coronary can fulfill the demands of sexual activity without evidence of significant strain."

Sex, the language of intimacy, is a part of life. It affects your psychological and physical well-being. In turn, physical and psychological health are reflected in your sexual functioning. You can't neglect one without neglecting all.

6
Thought Loops

For those who would ward off sexual problems and heighten sexual pleasure there are ways of reaching beyond the critical part of the mind to the primitive brain, which is attuned to the body's desires and interested only in their maximum satisfaction. Techniques of relaxation and concentration, which are well known through Eastern religions and philosophies, directly influence the brain's rhythms, and through this the central nervous system and the body's autonomous structure, making a new self-awareness possible. In this way, both mind and body can be prepared for sexual activity and for uninhibited intimacy with a sexual partner.

Yoga, in its many forms, and the other Eastern philosophies have always aimed at gaining full control of moods and emotions. The student has been told, if he took the toughest course, that he would learn to shut off thought as simply as turning a light switch. That he would be able to reach a state of perfect bliss in which both feeling and thought were completely shut out. To many a Western mind these promises seem incomprehensible and possibly undesirable. The rigorous and prolonged training needed to acquire these abilities also goes against the grain.

Thought loops let us have benefits of these Eastern practices in a fashion that is comfortable and understandable to the Western mind. The thought-loop technique will release you from the barriers that have prevented or short-circuited intimacy in the past. It will also give you greater freedom with your mind and greater relaxation with your body than you have ever known before.

The older and automatic parts of our brain have been made prisoner by our rational nature, the newer cerebral cortex, seat of our rationality. The older parts of the brain, the sympathetic and parasympathetic nervous systems, have to keep functioning automatically to run our breathing, heart rate, digestion, and the body's many other automatic functions, which the cortex is far too nervous to do properly. The job of the primitive brain is made even more difficult by the continuing alarms that the cortex sends it. Thou shalt work before play. Thou shalt plan ahead. Thou shalt not give in to desires. Thou shalt never give in to physical desires.

We can relieve the old brain of these unnecessary burdens by using thought loops. Thought loops can be learned alone. You don't have to know autohypnosis in order to use thought loops or benefit from their effects.

A thought loop is a set of phrases that you silently think. This repetitious thinking of a single idea is done most easily if it is thought of as a series of words on an endless loop of paper that goes round and round. Some people like to feel that they are reading the words from the paper strip. Others prefer to "hear" the phrase. Some just like to think it. All of these ways seem to work equally well. So make your own choice, and change to another when it seems desirable.

Training in the use of thought loops for free concentration is not difficult, although it does require time. Usually concentration is interpreted as bringing attention to a high degree of intensity, and centering this attention on specific goals. In contrast free concentration employs a casual mental attitude toward both methods and goals. The inner voices of your mind and body speak for themselves, without the vigilant censorship of the conscious brain.

This does not mean that you have no goals, but that these expand and improve as you learn about your inner self. You find that your body is a unity, not a collection of separate and independent parts. In a short time you will achieve efficient results with free concentration, even though you have no outside help.

You won't need it. Your own awareness of changes within you will be sufficient self-information. By the third or fourth day you will start to become aware of positive and healthy changes.

We are trained to be tense and alert throughout our lives. Because this training occurs unconsciously, it is difficult to overcome. Learning thought loops and free concentration involves a little time and effort at first. But once you have learned this technique it's something you can do at any time, anywhere, for relaxation and self-knowledge.

How to Start Thought Loops

As you start to learn these exercises you should find a quiet spot where distractions will be at a minimum. Later on, you will find you can do them anywhere regardless of the crowd and noise around.

Begin in bed, or sitting in a comfortable chair, dressed loosely or not at all. Lie or sit in a comfortable position with your arms at your sides, held loosely, and your legs slightly apart. If you are lying down, have a comfortable pillow for your head; if you are sitting, let your head hang down relaxed on your chest. In doing these exercises you should only allow one thing in your mind—a formula of thought loops which you will repeat mentally over and over. Your object is to discover your body and its sensations and pleasure in their entirety. But do not concentrate on anything other than the loops. These self-regulating, brain-directed exercises will do the rest as you allow yourself to be freely passive.

Before you begin each specific thought loop you should think to yourself, "I am at peace." It actually doesn't matter whether you are really at peace or not—you should be passive to this degree. If you try to force yourself to feel at peace, however, particularly on a bad day, you will accomplish the reverse of your desire.

The first loop to use is to think, if you're right-handed, "My right arm is light," over and over again to yourself. (If you're left-handed, begin with the left arm.) Don't talk out loud—just think. It's usually easier to accomplish the feeling of lightness and floating in either arm by softly touching or stroking it before you begin the exercise. This touching yourself will speed up the process of awareness and help your concentration greatly, for each body part. Some individuals find that they do not immediately experience a feeling of lightness in their arms. You may have a sensation of tingling, prickling, or coolness. Don't be concerned—you will feel the lightness sensation after a few trials.

After thirty seconds to a minute of this concentration you should arouse yourself. The order in which you do this is important. First, shake your arms vigorously, then take a few deep breaths. Finally, open your eyes. If you opened your eyes first, shut them again and go through the motions and breathing before opening your eyes.

Having done free concentration once you may want to go right back and do it again. This is part of our civilized drive, but it's not the right thing to do. You should wait at least an hour before you again do thought loops.

You can do these thinking activities alone, or with your intimate partner. Free concentration is an excellent preparation for intimacy for a single individual. It is also a way of deepening and improving an ongoing intimate relationship. A long-term couple, deeply and closely associated, will find that their thought loops for free concentration can be best done together. If you are single, however, don't feel that you must go out and acquire a helper to do them with you.

If you are alone—and this will include many intimates who are separated from each other for various workaday reasons—you can begin at once. Get into the proper comfortable position and begin the loop: "I am at peace . . . my right arm is light . . . I am at peace . . . my right arm is light. . . ." For your first time, try to keep up this silent mental state—exclusive of all other thoughts—for a minute. Those sixty seconds will seem a very long time. You will be surprised how accurately your mind keeps watch over the time, however, and tells you when to arouse yourself from free concentration.

Once you have begun to have a feeling of lightness or other change in your arm, enlarge the loop formula to, "My right arm is light . . . my left arm is light . . . both arms are light." You can usually make this progression about the fourth or fifth time you do free concentration exercises. Don't start the expansion until you are really noticing changes of sensation in your right arm, which may be a floating, a feeling of weakness, numbness, tingling, or simply a feeling of estrangement and detachment in the arm.

Gradually progress through longer, and deeper, periods of thought loops until you are able to focus your subconscious mind on peaceful and light feelings for four or five minutes at a time. Don't try to spend too long a time in any individual session; instead make several periods, say, six or eight a day, when you freely concentrate for a brief time.

Mutual Concentration

Intimate couples find that they prefer to have their partners play an active role. Unless you have practiced meditation before, this is probably the most natural way to learn the technique. After the partner who is to concentrate has made himself comfortable, he usually finds that he is flooded with distracting thoughts. These have nothing to do with the "I am at peace" loop or any of the specific instructions. We all want to be *doing something*. The idea of doing nothing is culturally abhorrent to us, and that's what free concentration seems to be—until you do it. The other partner should take the first thirty seconds to tell the concentrator the thought loop formula over and over. This enables the concentrator to realize that he is doing what he wants.

As the speaker says the loop, it should not be changed around, but stated personally, so that it can be absorbed directly and doesn't need translation. He should say, just as the subject himself thinks, "I am at peace. My right arm is getting lighter." In the brief time, thirty seconds, that the partner repeats these phrases aloud, the concentrator is learning to focus his thoughts and free himself from distractions. The partner's voice should not only say the loop, but convey the message of peacefulness. He should talk clearly, distinctly, and slowly enough to give that feeling to his partner. The way the loop words are said is just as important as the words themselves. No other words should be used at all. When the thirty seconds are up, the speaker should simply cease talking. The next time anything is said by either partner should be when the observer says that another minute or so has gone by and it's time to begin arousal.

The concentrator should then arouse himself by shaking his arms, breathing deeply, and opening his eyes. He shouldn't then jump up from the bed or chair, but take a moment or two in silence to reorient himself. He should get up slowly and walk about the room in a leisurely fashion. After a moment or two he will find that he seems to have refocused—that he has returned from the trip.

Intimates should not quiz each other about what went on. Even if you have a desire to discuss it you shouldn't in the early sessions, for the simple reason that you don't know what you're talking about. You have only begun to discover that there is a door within you which can be opened. You don't have the key that opens the lock; indeed, you don't even know where the handle is yet. Don't talk about the concentration episode—in fact, don't talk about anything for a few moments.

The concentrator, unwittingly, has demanded a great deal from his partner. He might make a cup of tea, or perhaps open a bottle of wine. While doing these little mechanical tasks he will better reenter humdrum existence. Then he can return to his partner and chat about something of interest to both or play a game of chess, or do whatever pleases them. After about thirty minutes or so you can reverse your roles and do thought loop exercises again. This time the former helper becomes the concentrator and the one who previously concentrated becomes the observer.

Learning thought loops with your intimate partner doesn't have to be a big production. Just set aside a little time when first one, and then the other, can briefly run through the thought loops for a minute or two. Your communication with each other will improve simply through this process. Once you have started you should try to find opportunities during the day for each of you, no matter where you are, to practice thought loops.

Most of our learning is done in schools under strict rules and set regulations. Don't carry these schoolroom attitudes into your thought loop experience.

We often prevent our success in life through trying too hard —we get in our own way. Our cortex is trying to run our affairs through our alarm system, whereas the relaxed parasympathetic nervous system can do it automatically. The French psychotherapist Émile Coué called the problems that arise from trying too hard the law of reverse effect. Trying too hard turns on the adrenal glands and turns off the parasympathetic nervous system.

The calm, relaxed attitude of a Zen meditator takes many years of effort to achieve. In meditation his brain is producing waves that give him inner peace and self-knowledge as a rich reward for his efforts. With thought loops you can experience much of the same sense of peace without strenuous training. This could happen the first time you try them, or it might take a few trials and errors before anything much seems to happen. Don't be concerned if you fumble.

Fumbling is not a catastrophe. It's simply a matter of learning. Laugh at your mistakes. You positively couldn't learn anything without making some.

You should be very specific about limiting the amount of time you spend in any free concentration session. Start with just a minute or two. Later, after about two weeks of practice, you might go longer, up to five minutes, but ten minutes should be the maximum for any session. The idea that this thought training will take a certain amount of your time day after day causes many people to think they should speed up their training. But it doesn't work this way. If you try to go too fast, you will experience the law of reverse effect.

Advanced Thought Loops

Once you have learned to induce changes of feeling in your arms you should progress to the second set of thought loop formulas, which begin, "My right leg is light." Then broaden this formula to include your left leg, and then both legs. Before you do this exercise you should stroke or touch your legs, just as you did your arms before you began to concentrate on them.

You will find that in both of these exercises there is almost always a feeling of warmth accompanying a feeling of lightness. If you like, you can add a statement on warmth to the statement on lightness, both for the arms and for the legs. (Sometimes people find that this concentration on warmth in their arms or legs brings them uncomfortable sensations of heat instead. This is easy to correct by concentrating on the idea of *slightly warm* rather than *hot,* which is usually what they have been thinking, instead of *warmth.*)

Some people beginning thought-loop concentration experience general reactions of dizziness or faintness. In a way this is excellent, because it shows they will be able to get very effective results from free concentration. But it's also uncomfortable, and doesn't have to be put up with. People with this problem can get away from generalized sensations by changing their instructions slightly to make them more specific. Instead of saying, "My right arm is light," they should say, "My right hand is light," or even, "My right index finger is floating." These more limited directions will produce the specific effect required without causing generalized sensations.

By the time you have worked out this much thought loop concentration, you will be aware of thoughts entering your mind "from nowhere." Often these concern old, long-forgotten injuries of your arms, legs, or other areas. You may also have had a desire to experiment to see which of your arms or legs was lighter by attempting consciously to lift them. Don't do this, because it lessens the effect of the concentration. You should allow your body to regulate itself without your conscious awareness.

Too often we act as our own observers, standing aside from ourselves and being detached. This is frequently true in sexual situations where we fear physical failure or performance difficulty. We increase these fears, and create negative thought loops through our worries. Free thought concentration is going to let you exist within yourself and operate those internal controls that have previously operated only in unconscious and unknown ways.

After you have gone through the exercises to make your arms and legs light and to produce sensations of change in your limbs, you should progress to a thought loop formula that will give you a general effect. The easiest is to say, in addition to your previous statements, *not* as a replacement, "It breathes me."

We all know that breathing is one of the normal bodily servo-mechanisms we use continuously and comfortably. Yet all too many of us, if asked to stop breathing consciously and just let our bodies take over, would panic—at least initially. Relaxation takes care of this; we *know*, really, that breathing is automatic, that we don't have to pay attention to it; it happens. This fact is emphasized in the thought-loop formula, "It breathes me."

This thought loop helps you integrate your entire body into your pattern of free concentration. You learn to feel that all of your body is breathing. Without specifically putting sensations of warmth into your thought loops you have an overall sensation of warmth, lightness, and elation. Any mistakes you may have made or indecisions you may have had about thought loops will vanish with this new self-awareness.

If you are doing these loops with your partner, have him place his hand half an inch away from your body between the bottom of the ribs and the navel, and start you off on this new thought loop that adds "It breathes me." "My arms are light . . . my legs are light . . . I am at peace . . . it breathes me." He should repeat this regularly, distinctly, and slowly for thirty seconds, just as he did in your first exercise, holding his hand motionless and close to your midriff. The closeness of your intimate partner will greatly contribute to your awareness of your whole body.

The next thought loop enables you to obtain specific genital awareness. Begin your formula by thinking first, "Both of my arms are light . . . both of my legs are light . . . it breathes me." After ten to twenty seconds, whenever the feelings of lightness are beginning, you should add to your formula *warmth* instructions. "Both my arms are light and warm, both my legs are light, free, and warm." Then go on to say, in whatever way it is comfortable, "My genitals are warm and free." You may find it easier to use slang terms, medical terminology, or even a personal word that you may have developed for your genitals. Before starting this exercise, stroke your arms, legs, and genitals to make all of your body parts feel alert and integrated.

The idea of deliberately inducing erotic arousal is frightening to some people. They feel that there is something wrong with it. You can get rid of such fears through free loops of concentration. Your body's need to express itself sexually is a continuing one, not something that turns on and off like a light bulb. You may already have experienced erotic fantasies and sensations in your earlier free meditations. These are not "dirty thoughts" but brain-directed associations leading toward self-expression. The number of sensual thoughts you have is often in inverse proportion to your previous repression of these thoughts.

One of your ideas in learning thought loops—we deliberately stress *idea*, because it should not be a goal, or your chief, overwhelming desire—has probably been to learn about the inner circuits that can free your sexuality. Let this come in its own time, freely, without pressure. And don't make the mistake of thinking that sensuality is solely a matter of genital awareness.

With free thought-loop concentration you perceive and appreciate personality facets in others that you have never been aware of before. You realize that intimacy and sexuality are not always the same. You learn to appreciate more deeply and intimately your relationships with members of both sexes—without any homophile concerns. You begin to build your own directives and your own ways of improving free concentration. Inevitably, your feelings will deepen and take on a new eroticism.

All of your thought loops should be done in a no-pressure, no-demand way. The reason for using "it" in these thought formulas is that "it" implies that the particular body part works automatically. You will find, in fact, that you have been thinking "it" rather than identifying the body part in words. The primitive brain is quite willing to be passively non-specific. The over-active cortex gets in the way when we concentrate directively and actively instead of passively. Not only should the thought loops be passive, but your entire attitude should remain passive throughout. Through this feeling of no demand you are resynchronizing your brain waves.

Psychosomatic Changes

Physical changes occur all through the body with each of these free mental exercises. Blood flow and skin temperature increase in the part concentrated on. Reflexes are improved and become more controllable. The effects of stress are greatly lessened both during and after this mental activity. These benefits alone provide a good reason for doing thought loops.

As you repeat each of the thought loops you should alternate them with the "I am at peace" loop. This will give you peace of mind—but not always in the way you might anticipate. In order to obtain this peace your body may need to release material that it has long stored. While this material is repressed and held back you cannot truly be at peace, even though you have forgotten why you cannot be.

Instead of a curtain of peace descending over you with your early exercises you may have a feeling of anxiety and unrest, or an episode of muscular tension or twitching. This is a sign that your brain is releasing some of its long-held tensions and moving toward peace. Don't fight it, in an attempt to win through to a state of relaxation. You will block the brain's ability to direct itself to free relaxation.

You may experience some momentary distress as this material is cast out of the body, like a splinter buried deeply in your tissues that suddenly surfaces. You may find yourself having a crying spell in the midst of a session, for no apparent reason. But there is a reason: you are cleaning out the scars left from some old wound.

Your past life will not pass before you in cinemascope with a lecturer pointing out the specific parts of your life that are causing your present troubles. Most of our inability to feel at peace doesn't come from specific past episodes, but from the total life experience. These are not necessarily logical or even sequential, to be remembered in a set order. They are the nonlogical assumptions and fears that we were taught as truths. They were accepted unquestioningly by the mind and they can only be discharged in the same vague and general way in which they were introduced.

When you're having one of these discharge periods you may feel that the thought loop is making you worse, not better. It is not. Using the loop, not discontinuing it, is the way to find the peace you seek. A discharge may seem to be a distraction from the exercise, but it is only a part of the total self-regulation process that you are acquiring.

If you have ever had any severe bodily injuries or emotional troubles you may find that during training episodes you feel pain in the area where you were hurt previously. Most of us try to suppress our pain sensations and ignore them as best we can. But the pain has left an impression in the brain which prevents full relaxation. During thought loop concentration you are allowing yourself to say, "Yes, it hurts," even though the actual hurt was long ago. The brain mechanisms operate to select, control, and terminate these safety discharges from those parts of the brain that need unloading.

The number of such discharges any person will have can be fairly well guessed by knowing what his life was like, and is currently like. An individual who has had a number of severe accidents in the past will need to unload many different pain experiences, which will probably take several free concentration sessions. A person who has been reared in an unloving environment will often have a similarly great number of discharge episodes. If someone, at the present time, is going through emotional stress, sexual deprivation, or business or professional preoccupations, these also may need a number of discharges. Unlike old scars, current sources of distress need to be dealt with directly if they are not to become a vicious circle of discharging problems and renewing them.

Whether you're feeling at peace, suddenly happy, or suddenly sad, you should not let your thought loops run beyond a brief time. If they are prolonged for fifteen or twenty minutes, patterns are set up in the brain that interfere with future success in free concentration. The people most likely to do this are those who have not noticed any changes and think that staying with the thought loops longer will achieve the desired sensations. What they are doing, of course, is trying to combine active and passive concentration all at once. It boggles the mind—and it certainly stops the thought loops from working.

Your Unique Brain

Many of your unique personal characteristics are fixed at birth. Nobody else has your fingerprints or your liver. And your brain is different from every other human brain for two reasons. Anatomically, the parts of your brain that carry out specific intellectual functions are not the same as the parts of another person's brain that carry out these same functions. Psychologically, your brain is undergoing constant changes, which are uniquely yours, from before birth until death. The way in which your brain responds to thought loops is going to be the most personal experience you can have.

You will start to listen to an inner voice that you have never before heard because of static from your cerebral cortex. This inner voice may seem to be giving ideas and thoughts in a disordered, even nonsensical fashion. This should not bother or frighten you. Human beings always learn far more in a prelogical and illogical fashion than they do by reason.

If you have a session of pain and problem unloading, you should let it go a few minutes before stopping. If you stop too soon you have forced your internal mechanisms to back up and will have to start all over again the next time. Don't rush, and don't prolong. Simply allow the self-regulating mechanisms of your brain to clear themselves and readjust. But you should not go on for longer than five or six minutes. This is something that has been learned from professional experience, and as yet there is no biological reason known for it. Empirically, however, it works.

You can design your own thought loops for many purposes. People have used them to get thinner by saying that fattening food no longer interested them and that they would exercise regularly. Others have used thought loops to increase their beauty, enjoy sexual fantasies, or gain more pep and energy, as well as to relax. Intimate partners can use thought loops to strengthen their union and to eroticize themselves and their partners. They can even share fantasies this way.

Many creative people are aware that their ideas come from "out of the blue." The word *blue* probably has a much deeper significance than any of us realize. In experiments on producing alpha waves, the first kinds of waves that the brain makes in free concentration, Dr. Barbara Brown, a California researcher, has used a system of different colored lights to indicate to her subjects when they are producing various kinds of brain waves. Everyone, without exception, chooses the blue light to indicate his alpha waves. "Out of the blue" may not mean dropping from the sky, but rather from out of our innate primordial intelligence.

7
The Bioloop

Bio-feedback is a recent scientific concept, based on the principle that every activity within the body is accompanied by an electrical or pressure change. Research is currently being carried on in many universities and medical centers utilizing electrical changes within the body to give individuals a unique personal education in achieving control of their brains, muscles, and other bodily functions. This is done by making an electrical connection through a machine that amplifies the minute voltage fluctuations within the body and displays these changes by means of lights, whistles, or other signals. Alerted to formerly automatic internal changes people are able to learn how to accomplish bodily alterations consciously. It is such a new mode of learning that no explanation has yet been found for this ability. It apparently is an inherent talent that has lain dormant until now.

There is another new learning process that thrives upon sensing and does not need electrical devices for amplification and display. It uses body pressure changes that have, in the past, been the means of brain and body control employed by practitioners of the Eastern mystical religions: Yoga, Buddhism, even Karate. We now have become aware that by paying attention to pressure changes, all these formerly secret and difficult ways of learning can be accomplished quickly and easily by nearly everyone. We have called this new learning process the bioloop. Meaning that we incorporate into it a governance over the body's functions that was previously thought to be automatic and un-controllable.

In various cultures special techniques of reserved, prolonged intercourse have been taught to the "inner circle" as a matter of religious expression. The Tantric practices of Yoga and Buddhism have been based upon the ability that a man could acquire to prolong and heighten sexual union with his female partner. The Persians practiced *karezza,* or coitus reservatus, for the same reason.

The archery of Zen, the blows of Karate and the exercises of Yoga are all designed to teach bioloop production through mus-cle actions. Once we realize that the same effect can be obtained more quickly and easily through bioloop mastery and personal understanding we are on the Western road to Eastern secrets.

Studies in the United States and Israel have shown that these Eastern techniques are accompanied by the production of spe-cific currents in the brain, called alpha waves. This particular wave appears when concentration and meditation is done, al-though no one knows whether or not it is the cause of this mental state.

Producing Alpha Waves

The alpha wave is a slow wave, of eight to twelve cycles per second, that originates in the back portion of the cortex and progresses to the forehead area. These waves are generated by all of us some of the time—when we are at peace and resting. Specialists in such concentration, such as Yoga, Zen, and Karate experts, can generate far more of these waves as a result of their training. Not just more brain waves, but larger and better syn-chronized waves appear in tracings made of their brain patterns. This takes years of practice to master—when their techniques are used.

Brain-wave studies, using the electroencephalograph, have

demonstrated that thought loops also produce better alpha waves. F. Rohmer and L. Israel of Berlin did recordings on a group that was to begin this mental exercise and found that at first they had a great number of disorganized, fast brain rhythms. When the loops of free concentration became established, there appeared abundant and regular alpha waves. Recent research has shown that these various modes of concentration and related mental functions play a decisive role in modifying the body's self-regulatory activity.

Dr. Barbara Brown has used an electronic technique—brain-wave bio-feedback—to teach people alpha-wave production in about six weeks. Using related equipment Dr. Joe Kamia of San Francisco has produced similar results—and refers to his group as "the fastest gurus in the West." Once alpha-wave production is learned you do not have to continue to practice the learning method—whether it began with thought loops and bioloops, or bio-feedback. The inherent skill of your body has been mobilized and will continue to operate under the direction of your faculties—for as long as you want.

In Dr. Brown's laboratory an individual is hooked up to a machine that reads brain-wave patterns. When alpha waves are produced the machine turns on a blue light. With a few waves the light is rather dim. As more waves are produced the light intensifies. This, somehow, teaches a person to make his own alpha waves.

A little easier to understand are the muscle-relaxing bio-feedback methods of Dr. J. Stova of Denver, and many others throughout the world. Several experiments have been made using electrical connections that reflect, and display, muscle tension. People with chronic headaches, due to frontalis muscle tension, have been trained to relax the muscles of their foreheads —and turn off headaches. Later tests have shown that they have also learned to produce alpha waves in a better and more synchronized fashion. Why not? Their training has been very similar to that of the Eastern experts.

Our nervous system consists of two parts, the central-voluntary system, and the autonomic-involuntary system. Through the first system, the brain controls the movements of the muscles of our arms and legs, and conscious thinking. Breathing, heartbeats, and erections were all basically uncontrollable reflexes run by the spinal autonomic centers. Neurophysiological research first discovered that the brain had some control over these autonomic functions—and the bioloop shows us how to exercise these dynamics.

The autonomic system is divided into sections, which work in opposition to each other. The sympathetic part is in charge of the alarm reactions that ready the body for "fight or flight" activities. The parasympathetic nerves regulate the more relaxed and peaceful portions of life—digestion, slow breathing, and heart rate—and sexual function. Our daily lives are filled with stimuli that trigger overactivity of the sympathetic system, and turn off the parasympathetic nerves. The pressures of "civilization" keep us in a constantly frustrating state of alarm. Heart attacks, diabetes, digestive upsets, and orgasmic failure are all the natural results of too much tension, too much sympathetic nervous tone.

The techniques of the bioloop can lead us out of this tension and into a state of tranquility previously thought to be possible only for those who spent their lives in meditation. Modern medical science now tells us that learning some such techniques for relaxation is imperative for physical and emotional health.

San Francisco's Dr. Meyer Friedman and his associates have demonstrated that a certain tense personality type, which they call "Type A," is more prone to heart attacks. The "Type A" individual is aggressive, ambitious, competitive, and time-driven. His muscular actions are abrupt and forceful, and often include a great deal of table pounding, explosive and uneven speech, fist clenching, and facial tautness. His time pressure is often self-imposed. His desire to gain his goals is often frustrated.

Just as our civilization keeps us in a constant state of stress, so it makes monotony and unvarying repetition too much a part of our lives. Monotony, in fact, can produce neurotic behavior. Liddell, in experiments done in England some thirty years ago, was the first to show that a regular mild discomfort occurring with unvarying frequency would produce a severe neurotic—and nonuseful—reaction. He subjected a goat to a schedule in which clocklike regularity was the essential feature.

Every ten seconds, when in certain specific surroundings, the goat would receive a shock to its right forefoot. At first the animal quite naturally lifted its leg to avoid the shock. But at the end of about ten days the goat began to have extreme difficulty in raising its foot out of the way of the shock, and a short while later was completely unable to move the foot at all in this situation. It had developed a tremor instead, which held the leg absolutely rigid so that it received the full force of the shock every time. Between times the goat moved about quite freely but once its internal alarm system rang and told the goat a shock was due, it acted neurotically to ensure the worst possible position and the full force of the discomfort. Since then many other research workers have used similar kinds of monotony to create neurosis in a variety of laboratory animals.

Thought loops, as we have seen, increase our ability to regulate the parasympathetic nervous system, and also give us freedom from the alarms that the cerebral cortex keeps sending out. The muscular relaxation that accompanies the production of thought loops also tells you something of how you work internally, and decreases the overactivity of the sympathetic nerves.

Learning to Breathe

We need to know the techniques of thought-loop relaxation in order to effectively learn about our own bioloops. Breathing is not a duty to perform before any other bioloop practice, but it should be done as an initial means of learning bioloops, because it is the easiest way to gain understanding of them. Breathing is an automatic action speeded up by the sympathetic nerves, and slowed by the parasympathetic. We don't have to admit the mystic powers of the breath that are part of Eastern philosophies to realize that this automatic function is one we can regulate whenever we want. Our entire system will reflect an increased parasympathetic tone through the conscious control of the breath.

This is the route by which the rest of the bioloops can be traveled.

The major muscle that controls breathing is the diaphragm. It should move up and down freely and fully to control your respirations. When we breathe unconsciously we usually do not have enough motion in this muscle, and the breaths are shallow. When you begin to control your chest movements, make sure to breathe in and out at as slow a rate as is comfortable. Anyone who breathes at a rapid and full rate will quickly knock himself out by hyperventilation. Too much air washes out the carbon dioxide in the lungs and causes muscle cramps, followed by unconsciousness. If you breathe at a rate of fourteen to eighteen times a minute this won't happen.

As you breathe in, push your diaphragm down. It will make your belly puff out a little, but don't be concerned. Wait—hold that breath. If you want to hold a little longer than usual, swallowing once or twice will slow down the desire to exhale. When you breathe out make it as complete, but as slow, as you can. A quick, forceful exhalation has been used by warriors for centuries as a means of maximum stimulation just before the battle is joined—sympathetic stimulation! All you need to do to achieve the reverse result is to maintain this cycle of relaxed respiration for a minute or two. This will give you the first step in control over your parasympathetic nerves, and eliminate the stress effects of high sympathetic tone.

As you breathe, notice the pressure changes within your chest, and in the skin and breasts and over it. Learn to be conscious and aware of these changes. This may be a first self-admission of biological function and of body pleasure. The feeling of enjoyment that some individuals have from smoking probably comes from awareness of the lung sensations that occur with inhalation. You don't need a cigarette to obtain this feeling—just be aware.

With this conscious control over your breathing you have made the first step toward bioloop understanding. This cannot be done in a demanding, right-now fashion. Only through full, free realization and self-absorption can you find this state. This is not a selfish kind of absorption, but a state of acceptance and passive giving of yourself to reflection. As you continue in this new state of consciousness you will begin to find other changes occurring within you. Allowed, they happen; demanded—there's nothing.

Sexual Bioloops

Just as the switch from involuntary to automatic bioloop breath control can be made, so can sexual faculties be discovered. This takes the same relaxed, unpressured, and reflective state. The mind must first become consciously aware of the changes that naturally occur, and the underlying muscular actions before you are able to form a full sexual bioloop. Erections, lubrication, and erotic sensibilities all respond to the free concentration formulas of thought loops. Looking, waiting, and watching for reactions is the certain way to break the loop. Allowing, not forcing, the sensations of lightness and warmth may be helped by adding a statement of *fullness* to the genital formulas. Saying, mentally, "I am at peace . . . it breathes me . . . my genitals are warm and full . . . ," strengthens these bioloops.

The genital thought loop is not the one to begin with. It is part of a progression toward erotic arousal that will be effective after beginning with the other thought loops. Some have found that they can do better with this state if they change the word *light* to *heavy*, for the genitals. Mostly, this seems to work for men. Females have been so diet and weight conscious that any mention of heavy can be upsetting. Do what works—for you.

In the sexual area the changes that occur are due to nerve action, blood vessel muscle reaction, and pressure changes—which all add up to erection. We need an understanding of these natural functions to find the "handles" of our personal bioloops, and that is easy to obtain.

One of the first changes to occur during sexual stimulation is erection. The mechanisms that cause the penis, labia, and clitoris to become erect are the same for both sexes. Nerves go from the spinal cord to and from these organs carrying messages along the same pathways to analogous structures. For both man and woman it's far easier to observe the reactions of the penis, just as it has been for scientists. Many detailed descriptions are available on the mechanism of penile erection, as compared to scattered and incomplete descriptions of labial and clitoral erections. As better instrumentation is developed this paucity of information on the female will be remedied. We don't need to wait for this. All the information we need is within ourselves. It can be helped by observing the male partner's reactions, and knowing that the female's are similar.

The male's erection appears to be an active, aggressive deed. It is not. To quote Dickinson, in *Human Sex Anatomy*, "It was a surprising paradox to discover that erection, or hardening, was started by a process of relaxation of spasm!" This spasm is a cramp of muscles in the small arteries, arterioles, that supply blood to the penis. The anatomy of the penis is such that it is always ready for an erection, restrained from it by nervous impulses from the sympathetic autonomic nervous system. When the impulses from the sympathetic nervous system are neutralized by parasympathetic impulses from the sacral division of the spinal cord, which flow out and relax this muscular spasm, erection occurs.

In the woman there is a similar erective mechanism that fills the labia minora and the shaft of the clitoris with blood. In women this erection process is preceded by lubrication of the vaginal walls.

In both sexes, sexual response is an automatic and sequential matter that continues to progress once a sufficient stimulus is accepted and continued. What this is going to be differs from culture to culture, and from person to person. The strongest stimulus is always that of touch in an intimate encounter.

There are two types of pressure changes that can be noticed and, once recognized, deliberately used to increase and prolong the pleasures of coitus. The first of these is the voluntary muscle pressure that can be gained from the use of the pubococcygeus muscle, the pelvic diaphragm. The second is more hidden—indeed, occult. Active concentration is necessary to isolate it before free concentration is possible to regulate it. This involves knowledge of the small smooth muscles in the male prostatic urethra, which regulate ejaculation.

Both men and women can easily learn control over the pubococcygeus muscle. We all make use of this muscle when we need to use the toilet, but have to wait. We deliberately delay nature's call by tensing this muscle. Most of us can tense the anterior, or frontal, portion to relieve bladder problems. We tense the posterior portion to postpone bowel movement. Each of us is aware of how these muscles work because we must be able to use them in these emergency situations. Without any deep or thoughtful training you can tighten them up right now, and relax them. Tightening and relaxing the pubococcygeus muscles should be a part of your daily routine, just like washing your face.

Tensing these muscles intermittently, during intercourse, causes the vagina to contract with heightened awareness and pleasure for both parties. It increases sensory feeling for both man and woman and amounts to a new caress. Stories of the penis being seized and captured by the vagina may have originated in the lurid and misinformed minds of those who heard about this technique for the first time. These muscles are not that strong—even if used daily for years. The history of man has yet to give us an authenticated case of penis captivatus.

Dr. Kegal of Los Angeles was the first to bring this ancient technique, supposedly one of the charms of the courtesans of ancient Greece, to the attention of current medical practice. He designed an instrument called the perineometer, a gauge which registers pressure changes within the vagina. Watching the needle change in the gauge acts as feedback for bioloop control. It has been used successfully over the years by many women who were previously having orgasmic difficulties. Since men and women alike can be aware of their internal muscle movements this device is no longer needed. Like much good science, Dr. Kegal's device has made possible the progress that causes its obsolescence.

The Oldest Bioloops

Going to the ultimate point in sexual ability involves using the muscles of the urethra as well as the pubococcygeus, to achieve control over ejaculation. This is an exclusively male concern. Some women can have a series of orgasms, with or without pauses, and still be able to continue copulatory activity. Men have only one, and they must then wait for their nerves to recover from a refractory, out-to-lunch state before their erective ability returns.

The Tantric writings on ejaculatory control are as obsolete as the perineometer. Their idea of female semen has been disproved by modern science. The results of their practices, however, were and are excellent, even though founded on false premises. The idea that the smooth muscle of the prostatic urethra can be moved by thought belongs to the Tantrists. As does the idea that women can control and decrease the size of the inner two thirds of the vagina, by using the similar smooth muscles of the vaginal wall. They were well aware of one of the basic principles of the bioloop, which is pressure.

The mysterious secret of those who prolong coitus indefinitely is that the man has learned to regulate the smooth muscle of his urethra and the woman those of her vagina. In both sexes these smooth muscles are under indirect control, and learning to manage them is not always as easy as using the directly controlled pubococcygeus muscle. The Yoga books call this art *Vajroli*, and state that it can be practiced by a man or a woman. For both, learning to control the pubococcygeus is a necessary intermediate step to regulating the smooth muscles.

Tantric yoga adds instructions for pressure—bioloop—education: "By means of a pipe, one should blow air slowly into the male organ. By practice the discharged *bindu* [semen] is drawn up. One can draw back and preserve one's own discharged *bindu.*" This Tantric practice has caused much argument. If a complete ejaculation has taken place, the semen could not possibly be drawn back into the body. Presumably, the semen would have been expelled from the glandular apparatus but not finally expelled from the body. However, the instruction is right, halfway. Pressure *will* teach bioloops. Blowing air into the male urethra can be hazardous, however, because infective bacteria may be blown into an area that has little ability to resist infection.

There are other and safer ways to acquire this ability over one's ejaculation. Once you have learned to contract the pubococcygeus muscle you have also learned how to make it relax. Ejaculation is always accomplished by involuntary, spasmodic contractions of the smooth muscle of the prostatic urethra. If you cause the pubococcygeus muscle to relax, you will remove the muscular pressure from this area—and stop emission. If you increase the pressure of the pubococcygeus muscle, on the other hand, you will hasten and heighten the ejaculatory process. It's so simple, so easy, and automatic to form the rest of the loop. Once the pressure for performance is taken away, the pressure from the pubococcygeus muscle will go away. The process is identical to the woman's anatomical control over the vaginal muscles.

Primitive men and women have known these bioloops since the dawn of time. We, the so-called civilized ones, have lost this knowledge because we learn about things—even ourselves—by dissecting everything into little bits of information. We view ourselves as a mass of separate, almost unrelated parts. A primitive man sees himself as a whole—nothing else. We have to make ourselves whole by reassembling the pieces and ceasing to think of them as parts.

We can regulate our bioloops and our automatic nervous system most effectively by following, in broad outline, the information given us by the Eastern mystics. They did not know about all the separate parts and made some errors that disturb the Western mind. But they were on the right track, and they got there. We, in our way, can get there too—by becoming whole again.

8

Here and Now —
I and Thou

Intimacy is possible only between real people whose minds and bodies and senses are tuned to the "here and now" and who can relate to each other, "I and Thou," with openness and honesty. Babies and small children can do this. But in the socialization process of growing up most of us lose the ability. We learn to wear masks, to play games, to please others, to manipulate, to compete, to worry about the future, to regret the past, to bestow words on each other, to act out roles, to use our fellow humans to gain our own ends.

If we learn these lessons well and practice what we have learned, we can become financially secure and emotionally invulnerable, both of which save a good deal of pain. We can also become bored and lonely, both very painful states.

How painful, and how common the pain, we can judge from the number of people joining encounter groups across the country in an effort to shed their shells and their pretenses, and make contact once again with their feelings and with other people. Psychologist Dr. Warren Bennis estimates that there are six million encounter group participants, and the movement is still growing.

Not everybody is happy about this. Encounter groups, known also as T (for training) groups, sensitivity or sensory awareness sessions, growth centers, and human potential experiences, have been sharply criticized from pulpits, in Congress, and by psychiatrists. At the same time their techniques have been used by churches, the government, educators, business, and psychiatrists. In fact, some of the nation's most outstanding educators and psychiatrists have been at the forefront of the encounter movement.

Some of the critics are shocked by the physical contact that takes place in some encounters and by the nudity that is sometimes part of the sessions. Others worry about mind control and behavior programming. The critic psychiatrists warn that many encounter leaders have little or no training and that the intense emotional environment of the encounter has triggered mental illness in some participants.

If you are going to become a participant yourself you should be aware of these criticisms. It is possible to get into a group with a poor leader. It is also possible to get out of the group and, usually, to find another. Though there are many prominent people in the human potential movement, and many leaders with long lists of degrees after their names, group leaders can't and shouldn't be judged by these credentials, say the authorities who work within the movement.

The movement is young and involved in new concepts, ideas, and techniques. Centers, like California's famous Esalen, have found that many professionals schooled in the old ways can't adapt to the new. And so they've been developing their own leaders, trained in encounter methods, choosing those with appropriate backgrounds and personalities.

The encounter movement started as an experiment in education and it is still that. Its purpose is to teach people how to develop their human potential so that their lives and relationships will be enriching and rewarding. Though sometimes called "therapy for normals," sensitivity groups are not to be confused with the group therapy used by psychiatrists to treat patients who are ill.

People often make this identification, which leads to misunderstandings. The critic psychiatrists complain that many disturbed people, who should be taking their problems to psychotherapists, are taking them instead to growth centers, and that the encounter groups aggravate the trouble instead of curing it. On the other hand, many psychiatrists in the movement send patients to encounter groups as part of their treatment.

As yet no one has adequately measured either the harm or the good that encounter groups do. Critics call them harmful because participants have been known to commit suicide or to seek help from psychotherapists after encounter experiences. But people commit suicide after and during psychotherapy, too. And most suicides are driven to this desperate act by life alone.

One in every four people walking the streets as normal is said to be in need of psychiatric help. If a sensitivity group gives one of these persons enough insight to seek psychiatric help, then it seems odd that the experience should be faulted for this reason. It is also possible that the troubled persons, looking for help, didn't find it in encounter and so sought psychiatric treatment.

It would be interesting to know how many people contemplating suicide, or an escape into mental illness, were given a new lease on life through their group experience. The only place this has been measured is in Synanon, where the encounter group has been used in the rehabilitation of drug addicts with remarkable success.

Learning to Feel

There are many different kinds of encounter groups. They not only differ in content but also in emotional impact, which is often greater the longer the experience lasts. Some sessions are an evening long. Others last a full day. Marathons usually extend over a weekend.

The Synanon games, which many "straights" play with great enthusiasm, are mostly verbal. A lot of time is taken up with getting rid of what they call the "garbage." The garbage includes your hostilities and defenses. The group, of from six to twelve people, gets rid of hostility by verbally attacking the defenses of one member after another. When barriers are down, and antagonism dissipated, positive feelings surface. Then group members who started out screaming insults and challenges and obscenities at each other are able to relate warmly and constructively.

Not all verbal groups are as abrasive as the Synanon games. The goal of some is to teach participants to truly listen to themselves and to others, to respond to and communicate feelings rather than making judgments. Since most of us have been taught to hide our feelings, even from ourselves, merely learning to identify and label the emotions we experience while listening is an involved learning process.

Getting out of your head and in touch with your true feelings is the goal of most encounter groups, but they go about it in different ways. Instead of having participants shout down each other's communication barriers, California psychologist Paul Bindrim has them strip away their protective armor with their clothes. In the buff everyone is equal and equally vulnerable. Much of Bindrim's encounter in the nude takes place in a warm Jacuzzi bath, or "womb pool," which lends an elemental security to the new experience of being completely revealed, bodily and emotionally.

In most nude encounters physical contact is encouraged but rules against sexual intercourse are strictly enforced. In this way participants relearn responses to the naked body. With the goal of orgasm removed, the nude group members are free to concentrate on the sensuous and communicative possibilities of their unclothed togetherness. People become persons instead of sexual objects.

Other encounter groups use psychodrama, dance, art, games, massage, and other physical techniques to encourage participants to release and communicate their emotions. Since we often use words to conceal our true feelings we sometimes find it easier to communicate them nonverbally.

Both verbal and nonverbal encounter methods are used by many groups not in the human potential movement. Among the first to use the techniques was the aerospace industry, which found that it could solve its technical problems much more easily than its personnel problems. Executives and workers in other industries too have recently been learning to work together, instead of at cross-purposes, through T-groups.

Teachers, parents, and pupils have been crossing the generation gap in encounter groups. And blacks and whites have been crossing racial barriers in the same way. At the very heart of the women's liberation movement are "consciousness-raising cadres" in which women explore and compare the experience of being female in a male-dominated world.

The human potential movement, too, uses the methods it has developed to help participants through many life adjustments. There are groups for couples contemplating marriage and for those contemplating separation, as well as for the divorced. Special sessions may deal with middle age, retirement, attitudes toward money, dreams, fashions, politics, ecology, religion. With others interested in the same subjects, group members work through stereotyped ways of viewing the world around them, and the problems that impinge on their lives, and search beyond them for valid and creative methods of responding to these challenges.

Joining a Group

Most encounter groups are fairly unstructured happenings. The leader is there, really, as a facilitator who helps the group members shed their initial shyness and start relating. Since each group is different, the facilitator matches his techniques to the members. For this reason it's impossible to describe a "typical" encounter group. But this is the sort of thing that might happen to you if you were to join a group.

You would find yourself with half a dozen or a dozen strangers, informally dressed for action, and barefoot or in stocking feet. Forming a circle with the others, you might be asked to close your eyes and "feel" the space around you, in front, above, below, to the side, and behind. While exploring your bit of space, yours hands will occasionally touch those of your neighbors, exploring theirs.

Afterward the leader will ask you to think about the way you felt, making these contacts, and to verbalize for the group if you wish. Were you annoyed when you found someone intruding on your space? Or apologetic when you felt you were intruding on his? Did you enjoy the accidental contact or did you hastily withdraw from it? This little five-minute experience can give you a great deal of insight into the way you relate to others.

After that you may be asked to meet the rest of the group by closing your eyes and moving around the room. As you touch someone else you will stop and get acquainted, not in the usual way, by looking and speaking, but rather through the use of the other senses—touch and smell and hearing.

You will be surprised at the things you can learn about others in this way, realizing too that they are learning the same things about you. You will become aware of the other's breathing, the temperature of his skin, the tautness of his muscles. These will tell you whether he is relaxed or tense, enjoying this experience or frightened of it, afraid of contact or eager for it.

Getting acquainted may also involve milling around the room with the eyes open, looking at each person you meet, and telling him of what he reminds you. This may be a color, food, a historical personage, an animal, a season of the year. By the time this is over your feelings could be intense. Has everyone in the group seemed threatening to you, so that you described each as "red," "fire," "bull," "cannon"? And have you had to recognize that you remind others of "winter," "ice," "blizzard," "North Pole"?

Now, as the group seats itself, usually on the floor, the feelings generated will come out in words. "Why did you say 'not' when you looked at me?" someone may ask someone else. "Not what?"

"Knot. A knot. You look as if you were all tied up in yourself. Do you feel that way?"

"Maybe, a little."

"You look as if you always felt that way," someone else may chime in.

The leader will keep the group's attention focused on one participant at a time. When the person who was thought to resemble a knot has touched his up-tight feelings and expressed a wish to be rid of them, the group may stretch him as he lies on the floor by pulling on his legs and arms and shoulders until he feels relaxed and physically loose. This physical relaxation will be reflected in his emotions.

Someone who feels overwhelmed by the group may be truly overwhelmed as the group tries to keep him enclosed in a tight circle, or pinned on his back on the floor, so that he must struggle to release himself. Someone who feels left out may be forced to fight his way into a circle closed against him.

This physical representation of the emotional state keeps the person from fighting down the full intensity of his feelings. He *has* to feel deeply. And the struggle to get out of the physical predicament can also release him from the painful emotion.

Sometimes it isn't struggle that is needed. A person may be so out of touch with himself that he can't sort out what he feels. Then the group may assist by acting out his feelings for him. Different ones, playing different parts of his nature, may quarrel and struggle to get near him. Watching, he will be able to visualize how he rejects some feelings while clinging to others for security. Or a person who feels unloved may be lifted by all the members of the group and rocked in the cradle of their arms.

These are the kinds of things that happen in encounter groups. Their purpose is to rid the participant of the weight of masks and armor he usually feels he must carry in order to play his role in the world. Free to be himself, he finds that he can experience each moment more fully and relate to those about him in an honest, open, and meaningful way.

It takes more than one encounter experience to accomplish this, and some people never do manage. Encounter isn't for everyone. Whether or not it's for you, you will have to decide. If you get into the spirit of it, it is excellent preparation for intimacy. So are many of its methods. If you can't attend encounter groups, or as a supplement to your encounter experience, you may want to use some of the methods by yourself and with your intimate partner.

It sometimes takes a great deal of effort and practice to find the authentic self again after the years we have been trained to reject it. We may even be afraid to make the effort, having been taught our real selves are unworthy. But we can't commune intimately and deeply with another until we have discovered, and know, and value, our own intrinsic persons.

"Joy," writes Dr. William C. Schutz, "is the feeling that comes when one realizes his potential for feeling, for having inner freedom and openness for full expression of himself." The greater the inner freedom each of us has, the greater the capacity for a meaningful intimate relationship.

Sensitivity Training for One

One of the problems that each of us has is identifying, grasping, and coping with real feelings. All our lives we've been taught to bury, deny, and camouflage them.

The boss has humiliated us, but we can't let it show. So we pretend it didn't hurt, and take it out on the cat—or the children —when we get home. We're elated because Sally called and invited us to a party, but we fear that if Sally knew how we felt she might think herself "one up," so we camouflage our delight with indifference and ultimately lose it.

A way to find out what you are feeling at any moment is to start humming. Just hum a few notes at random. After all, there are only so many tones in the scale. Shortly the notes you are humming will form a melody that will give you a clue to your feeling. You may not be able to make yourself hum at all. That also is a clue to your feelings.

Follow the clue, acknowledge the emotion, accept it, experience it, trace it back to its origin. If it's a good feeling, cling to it, and memorize the way it affects your body. Note your breathing, your stance, the set of your muscles. For just as feelings affect your body, so your body affects your emotions. In the future you'll be able to tempt back the good feeling by imitating the way it affected you physically.

In our civilized world the feeling most often buried and denied is anger. We cut it off at its source, refusing to acknowledge it. But every emotion has physical manifestations. Anger prepares us to fight. It pours adrenalin into the bloodstream and alerts the muscles.

The best way to get rid of this anger is to admit it, to yourself and to the person who made you angry. Sometimes you can't admit it to the other, of course. You're not allowed to clobber somebody, especially if he's your boss. But you can, even while he's making you angry, expel that anger physically through exercise.

Contract your stomach muscles for a count of ten. Then loosen them. Contract again. Or exercise your pubococcygeus muscles a dozen times or so. These exercises will keep your anger from turning into a headache or a stomach ache.

If exercise isn't enough to rid you of your hostility, then let it out by yelling in the car as you drive home from work. Really give the boss hell. Or the world, if that's the way you feel. If you belong to a car pool then skip the martini when you get home and take a long shower and yell there, while the running water drowns you out. Or beat the bed, or a couch, until you are exhausted.

When one is uncertain of his feelings this often shows up as difficulty in making a decision. Do I want to go out or stay home? Should I keep this job or look for another? Should I marry Jane or buy a boat?

You can sometimes sort out the feelings and understand the emotions involved in the decision if you fantasize the choice in your mind. Pretend there are two people arguing in your head and listen to their points of view. You may be surprised to see that one of these imaginary persons is much larger than the other —yourself today as opposed to yourself as a child, or perhaps a parent as opposed to you. Once you understand where your conflicting emotions come from you'll be better able to recognize those that are authentic.

This is an excellent exercise for someone who is wondering

whether or not to engage in an intimate relationship. Try it, if this is your situation, and find out whether you yourself are objecting to intimacy or whether it is a parent, dominating you still over years and, perhaps, miles.

Another way to touch your real feelings is to pay attention to the seemingly inconsequential thoughts that enter your mind. If you are concentrating on your work and suddenly think of Cousin Jerry, don't dismiss him. Try to find out why he appeared. It may give you insight into your attitude toward your work.

Playing it the other way around, if you find yourself feeling uneasy, and don't know just why, try free associating, as if you were telling a psychiatrist whatever came into your mind. And then play the psychiatrist and try to analyze the random thoughts. You'll find they often make amazing sense and explain a mood that was formerly inexplicable.

Just as you can learn a lot about another by talking to him, so you can learn a lot about yourself in the same way. Are you feeling depressed? Have a headache, or indigestion? Sit down with whatever part of you is in trouble and talk to that part of your being. Ask your head why it is aching, and listen to the answer. Or ask your stomach why it is in pain. Consult your whole body about your feeling of depression. If you can discover the emotional reasons for these psychosomatic ailments you can often prevent and cure them.

Whatever affects your mind affects your body too. It's an endless round-robin. Grief can set your muscles in a way that contributes to feelings of self-pity. Joy can have the opposite effect. Fear can make you run. And running, at the first instance of fear, can make you more afraid.

In contrast, assuming a posture of courage can make you brave. And assuming a posture of joy can make you joyful. But you must know which posture does which.

To understand the way body movement and stance alter mood, put some music on the record player, preferably something like a symphony that has many varied affects and rhythms. Then take off your clothes and dance to the music. Don't be surprised if you feel odd; that will tell you something about yourself too. Every now and then stop dancing and hold your pose, as if you were a statue. Identify your feeling. Are you sad, happy, exalted, humble? When you know how you feel, psychologically, make yourself aware physically. Concentrate on each part of your body from your toes to your head. Which muscles are taut and which relaxed? Memorize this body posture.

Then start dancing again. When you are aware of a change of mood, stop and become a statue. Identify your feeling and explore your posture, noting the ways it differs from the posture that contributed to your first mood. When you have done this several times, try dancing yourself into a particular mood by using the movements and postures you now know are the physical manifestations of that feeling. After a few dancing sessions you should be able to posture yourself into a wanted emotion at any time.

Encounter for Couples

Many couples find that encounter techniques are helpful in increasing their understanding of each other and strengthening emotional ties. You might like to try some of them with your intimate partner.

The nonverbal greeting when you come together after hours apart can bring you closer together in a short time than mountains of words. Don't ask, "How are you?" Let your eyes and hands discover as they explore the face, the throat, the shoulders, and body of your partner. As you do this "map reading," you'll find both of you relaxing and forgetting everything but each other.

Sometimes when the two of you are together physically you still feel far apart. The games you played in childhood will often help you back to the "Here and Now—I and Thou." "Pease Porridge Hot" is a game that provides contact and often laughter. Thumb wrestling and arm wrestling are ways to rid yourselves of negative feelings.

For the thumb wrestle, start to shake hands but, instead, bend your fingers and hook them into your partner's hooked fingers, free thumbs on top. Raise your thumbs and let each try to pin the other's thumb down for a count of three.

For the arm wrestle it's best to lie on the floor on your stomachs. Place the elbow of one arm on the floor in front of you, next to the elbow of your partner, forearms up straight in the air. Lock fingers while each tries to force the other's fist to the floor.

When your feelings toward your intimate partner are strained or ambivalent, an excellent way of bringing them to the surface where you can handle them verbally is to use the encounter technique of the press. First one of you presses the other to the floor. You must get him all the way down, lying on his back. He can cooperate or resist, depending on how he feels.

Once he is down, you help him back to his feet. Then he presses you to the floor. After which he helps you up. When you have completed the exercise each of you will want to talk about how you felt about being subdued, doing the subduing, being helped up afterward, and helping the other to his feet. You'll usually find that your reactions and feelings during this exercise duplicate facets of your relationship. You will be able to understand them and talk about them more freely once the press has demonstrated them.

In talking out problems you will also—and always—want to use the encounter technique of listening. That means listening without judging so that you can repeat to your partner what he has said to his satisfaction. After that you tell how his words made you feel. Again without judgment. Only then do you present your arguments. After which he must repeat *them* to *your* satisfaction.

This is difficult to do, but well worth the effort for the understanding it brings. Strangely, one of the most difficult things to learn is the honest reporting of your feelings. Both partners must always know where the other is emotionally.

Very often intimate partners will verbalize the feelings they think the other wants to hear rather than the ones they are feeling. "I'm sorry," one will say, when he isn't at all. When you do this you transmit two sets of signals, confusing your partner and doing nothing to help clear the air.

We also make judgments and call them feelings. Perhaps the most common of these between intimate partners is, "I feel you don't love me." That isn't a feeling, of course. It's a judgment of the partner's feeling, based on insufficient evidence. Tapping your own feeling and communicating it to your partner will do more to bring about understanding than trying to guess his emotional state.

You may feel unloved. Or maybe unlovable. And the reasons you feel that way may have nothing to do with your partner. Blaming him for your unhappiness puts him on the defensive. Telling him about your state of mind, by honestly reporting your feeling, gives him a chance to help you out of your predicament.

Sometimes you can't verbalize a feeling or understand what your partner is trying to tell you. Then another encounter technique can come in handy. Act out the feeling for your partner by doing physically what the feeling impels you to do. This is often a more effective communication than words.

And don't forget the encounter technique of the "womb pool." It's unfortunate that our homes aren't equipped with Japanese baths. Couples who have them claim they are the greatest quarrel resolvers ever invented. But you can do the same thing with your tub. Fill it and invite your partner to share it with you. Touching each other in the warm relaxing water will soon bring sensations of peace and love. There is no speedier way to get to the "Here and Now—I and Thou." And there are few finer ways to prepare for making love.

9

The Intimate Encounter

Many people are just like encounter groups—they separate sensitivity and sex. The same couple who spends an evening at an encounter group, touching and being touched, will go home to bed and have sex, forgetting their sensitive bodies as they concentrate exclusively on their genitals and the goal of orgasm.

Indulgence in both the encounter group and sex are justified because each had a purpose. Through the encounter the partners sought to become more alive, so that they could get more out of life, or improve their relationship, or their communication with others. Through sex they sought orgasm to relax them, or produce a good night's sleep, or prove that they were sexually capable or desirable, or because *he* thought *she* wanted it, or because *she* felt *he* wanted it, or because they hadn't had it in quite a while.

Quite possibly as the future brings more leisure we will stop insisting that every activity have a purpose and find the pleasure of the moment reason enough for the moment. Until then, the union of sensitivity and sex, which we call intimacy, can be justified because it has important purposes, pleasure among them.

For one thing, sex is just plain more fun when the whole body and personality are involved. It's more exciting and mentally and physically stimulating. And for those who like to use each shining hour for maximum benefit it promotes health and well-being, and strengthens the couple's pair bond. Most important for today's sexual athletes, it removes the pressure to perform and with it the proneness to performance failure that so often mars and shortens their sex lives.

Sadly, in our society, few people have ever known erotic closeness that was not tainted by the pressure for performance. This pressure is part of the adolescents' necking and petting sessions, and of the hampering baggage carried on the honeymoon. Because it looms so large over our sexual encounters couples who wish to rid themselves of this deterrent to sensuous pleasure must relearn, as adults, the sensuality that was naturally theirs as children.

Fortunately this can be done, even after sexual pressures have brought on sexual failures, as Masters and Johnson have demonstrated in their treatment of sexual inadequacies. But how much better to avoid the failures by exchanging pressure for intimacy before trouble starts. In this way sexual pleasure is enhanced and sexual capacity increased, strengthened, and prolonged.

To understand how this works, it is helpful to understand the way the pressure to perform fails to work. Sexual response is a natural reaction to sensuous excitation. You might compare it to the gastric stimulation that occurs when you sit down to a meal.

The smell and sight of the food have a psychological impact. They remind you that you are hungry, and you fantasize how delicious the meal will taste. This prompts physical changes within you. Your mouth salivates and your stomach produces digestive juices. If you are to enjoy the food, all these things must happen. You can't consciously force them to do so, but you *can* interfere with these reactions.

Suppose you consider the meal a performance test. You feel it important to impress the host and hostess, but you fear you'll use the wrong fork or spoon, tangle awkwardly with the artichoke, and spill gravy on the tablecloth. All these fears can interfere with your enjoyment of the meal everywhere along the line. They can take away your appetite and prevent salivation and efficient digestion.

As a result, instead of experiencing the pleasure you anticipated you end up with heartburn. And the memory of your discomfort causes you to approach the next meal fearfully, too, so that it also turns out disastrously.

This is the same kind of thing that happens when concern for performance interferes with your appreciation of sensuous stimulation during the act of sex. What was meant to be a natural, total body reaction to an increasing input of sexual stimuli becomes something less than that if you block erotic input by concentrating on performance.

You can't respond to something to which you refuse attention, so what you are doing when you try to perform sexually is to imitate response and force your body to behave as though it had been allowed to experience the buildup of sensations necessary for natural sexual excitement and release. The resulting sexual impairment can be as slight as diminished appetite or enjoyment, or it can become a full-fledged case of sexual indigestion. In any case the disappointment, small or large, conscious or unconscious, compounds your fears for the next sexual encounter.

The male can hardly savor erotic feelings while he monitors his performance and that of his partner, striving to rush her response while he delays his own in order to satisfy her. Nor can she respond to much but this dual concern on his part, and on hers too. Will she be able to will an orgasm before his ejaculation terminates sexual contact?

To complicate matters neither may be giving the other maximum stimulation simply because they have never become erotically acquainted. And this is true of couples who have been together twenty years. Neither knows the sensitive places, or the kind of caress, that would turn the other on. Very often neither knows his own body well enough to instruct the other.

The Language of Intimacy

To reawaken and sensitize your own body, to get acquainted with the body of your partner, to change sex from mechanical manipulation to intimate communication, it is necessary to learn to relate physically without demands or goals. It is also delightful to do this. The way is through caring contact.

Caring contact is the language of intimacy. Practicing it, a couple learns to give and receive pleasure from each other's bodies and to trust their natural, physical response to this pleasure to bring them sexual ecstasy. Caring contact can eliminate the pressure for sexual performance and the fear of intimate physical contact for its own sake alone. Most important, caring contact can fulfill the deep human need for a total emotional and physical intimacy with another.

As with all lessons, caring contact must be learned a simple step at a time. The needs are privacy, a pleasant atmosphere, a bed, a bottle of body lotion, and two intimate partners willing to set out together on an erotic adventure. Let the woman be responsible for the preparations at first, but not without consulting her partner.

Does he like soft music in the background or does he prefer the sound of the wind at the windows? Does candlelight relax him or does its flickering flame disturb either partner? Above all, she should be sure that the scent of the body lotion appeals to both.

Scent is so important sexually, and we know so little about which odors arouse us, that scientists in Great Britain have found that conception rates fall every year after the holidays when women start wearing the scents they received for Christmas. So choose the lotion together, both for odor and texture.

Some of the after-bath moisturizing body lotions are excellent. Baby oil is good, with the addition of a little of your favorite scent. Or you might prefer a mixture of vegetable and baby oil if you are going to concoct your own. Vaseline is too sticky and tends to draw moisture out of the skin. The lotion should be kept in a warm place. Prior to the first caring contact session a generous amount of it should be poured into a small bowl or wide-mouthed jar and placed at the bedside.

The woman makes these arrangements, and initiates the first session, because women are usually more sensitive to their surroundings than are men. If she prepares the room and the bed he will learn, for the future, the kind of atmosphere she likes.

Also this gives her a chance to cover the sheet on which they will sleep with a special one for their lotioned bodies.

But more important, preparing for caring contact will start the movement of her thought loops. Fantasizing and anticipating the pleasure she is going to give and receive will put her in a sensuous frame of mind. Making the overtures, luring her partner into the caring contact session, and actively giving him pleasure with her caresses, will give her practice in initiating physical intimacy. All these involve a sexual assertion our culture has usually denied the female.

Her initiative also gives the male a chance to play a new and unaccustomed role. He is the seduced rather than the seducer, the pleasured rather than the performer. Perhaps for the first time in his life he is permitted to be passive in an intimate encounter.

Bathing or showering together is an excellent way to start a caring contact session. It provides a definite break from routine activities. It's relaxing and it puts partners in touch with their own and each other's bodies. Soap and scrub, and rub and towel each other. But with two prohibitions, at least for the first two sessions. Not during preliminary bathing, nor during the sessions themselves, should the genitals or breasts be touched or intercourse be initiated by either partner.

These may appear to be harsh rules but they have a reason. You already know that you have sexual feelings in your genitals. The object of the first caring contact periods is to allow you to discover and enjoy the eroticism of the rest of your body, including your fingertips. You might think of it as genitalizing your body—developing its sensuality so that it becomes an integral part of your sexual response.

The prohibition on intercourse is to break the pattern of demand for sexual performance that you've learned to associate with intimate bodily contact. Both of you should accept that contact as rewarding of and by itself. If you know there is to be no orgasmic denouement of the physical intimacy you have experienced, you will find other ways to express the closeness you feel. Holding, stroking, kissing, falling asleep in each other's arms, can be satisfying and love creating.

Just to put you both at ease, the caring contact session can start with a massaging by the female of the male partner's neck and shoulders. Let him lie face down on the bed while you, the woman, dip up some of the lotion and warm it in your hands. Then use it as a massage lotion, rubbing it into his neck and shoulders until the muscles seem to relax.

Now begin gentle caresses down his back, stroking lightly with one hand while you dip up more lotion and warm it in the other. The light touch is best, for the nerve endings that transmit pleasure are close to the surface of the skin. Pressing too hard anesthetizes them.

Except when you are dipping up and warming more lotion, use both hands for caressing, with fairly long slow strokes. When you dip up more lotion, always keep one hand in contact with your partner's body. It is important not to break the communication between you. Feel the texture of his skin beneath your fingertips. Remember, you are genitalizing them too. Let the feel of him run from your fingertips up your arms and into your body. Concentrate on what you are doing. Watch his reactions. Where does he seem to be most sensitive? In the armpits? Where the buttocks meet? In the folds of the knees? Watch, but don't ask. Asking is a demand.

You, the male partner, must feel no demands. You are to pay attention only to the pleasure you are receiving from the caressing of your body. Any response to that pleasure should be a natural, involuntary response. You are not trying to please your partner by showing her how much she is pleasing you. You are concentrating exclusively on your erotic sensations.

If there are ways you want these increased, let your partner know. If you can do so, put one of your hands over hers and indicate, by lifting or pressing down, that you want a lighter or firmer touch. Or place her hand where you wish it would linger longer. When you feel you would like to roll over, do that, and let her caress your face, and neck, and chest, and abdomen, and sensitive inner thighs. You may find that even your feet, particularly the spaces between your toes, are sensuous.

When your body is vibrant with the sensations she has brought to you, change places with her. Now it is your turn to give the pleasure, and her turn to receive it. Don't assume that because you are male you know where her erogenous zones are and how to stimulate them. This is not a woman out of a book. She is unique and individual. Her most erogenous zone may be in the small of her back or under her chin. Together you will discover it, and all the other sensuous areas of her body.

During the second session of caring contact you may want to vary the caressing. The heels of the hands can be used for stroking, as well as the fingers. So can the fingernails, very gently. So can the cheeks of the face, the hair, the lips, the tongue, the breath. Blowing and licking and sucking can also be caressing. After the second session when the breasts and genitals are included in the caring contact, they will be particularly stimulated by the oral caresses. And many men will discover for the first time how erotically sensitive their nipples are. Women's breasts, soft and supple, give exciting caresses. There are all kinds of ways of caressing. Let your fancy roam.

HOW TO GIVE A WOMAN PLEASURE

With the third session of caring contact, when the genitals are included, the male should initiate the caresses, with the female as the pleasure receiver. Caressing of the genital area should be in addition to body caresses. The genitals should be approached slowly and gently by stroking the inner thighs upward toward the genital area.

It is when this area is approached and caressed that it is well to remember again that there must be no demands, and no goals, and no preconceived ideas on the part of the partner giving pleasure as to what constitutes pleasure for the other. Each learns this as he gives. Each will also learn best where and how to provide stimulation if the receiving partner places a hand on the caressing hand to guide it and regulate the firmness of the touch.

As the male approaches the genitals he should first explore the pleasure areas around them. The closed outer lips are susceptible to caress. The perineum, between the genitals and the anus, is a particularly sensitive area. Softly caressing the hairy mons pubis, just above the genitals, will usually cause the outer lips to open so that the whole mons area above the vagina is accessible for stroking.

This genital tissue around the clitoris is the most sexually sensitive in the female body and is the place to which most women confine their stroking when masturbating. With caring caresses here the man may well bring his partner to orgasm.

But he must remember that the tissues of the vulva, which he is stroking, are extremely delicate and highly endowed with nerve endings and sexual receptor cells. A harsh touch here can produce discomfort instead of pleasure. A soft, teasing technique usually provides the greatest stimulation.

He should follow the directions of his partner's guiding hand. And not by gesture, word, or question should he put any pressure on her to respond in any way to the pleasure he is providing. She can't give herself completely to the sensations she is experiencing if she feels that he has set goals for her or expects an expression of appreciation.

This is his opportunity to learn her body's natural reactions to sexual stimulation. The first is the unseen lubrication of the vaginal walls. He can note it by running his fingers down the natural path between the vulva's inner lips to the opening of the vagina. Inserting a finger here he will feel the moisture. Now he has a natural lubrication to use in caressing the sensitive clitoral area.

Unless his partner indicates otherwise, he should confine finger manipulation of the vagina itself to dipping up lubrication for his caresses of the more highly erotic tissues that surround the clitoris. As he does so he will see the outer lips of the vulva expand, open wider, and flatten away from the entrance to the vagina. The inner lips will seem to erect as they engorge with blood and increase in size forming a natural channel to the vagina, which they lengthen with their enlargement.

The clitoris also erects, beneath the hood formed by the joining of the vulva's inner lips just below the mons pubis. Though the tiny clitoris is the center of sexual sensation for the woman, the man should not stimulate it directly unless she guides his hand to do so. There is such a narrow line between stimulation and irritation of the clitoris that most women don't manipulate the organ directly during masturbation. As stimulation of the area around it continues, the clitoris protects itself from direct contact by retracting under the mons pubis.

With more caressing, either manual or oral, the outer third of the vagina engorges with blood and opens toward the still expanding inner lips. Both deepen in color, indicating that orgasm is imminent if sexual stimulation is continued. Orgasm itself will consist of rhythmic contractions of the vagina and the area around it, often including the anus.

Many women like to have one orgasm after another. If this is so of the female pleasure receiving partner, she may indicate a wish for intercourse at this point in caring contact. Or she may prefer simply to be stroked and held close. This yearning for closeness after orgasm seems to be a natural need on the part of the female. Studies show that after intercourse her body continues seeking contact with the body of her partner, even during sleep.

Satisfying a woman's desire for intimate physical contact after orgasm is one of the ways a man can show her most effectively that he cares about her as a person, not just as a sexual object. If he abruptly terminates contact after climax he leaves the woman still emotionally unsatisfied and frustrated.

If intercourse has closed the first phase of caring contact, the couple may want to put off the woman's caressing her partner until another time. Caring contact should never be continued to the point of exhaustion, disinterest, or boredom. And its procedures should be considered flexible enough for spontaneous innovations. The only rule that can't be broken is the one against demand for performance.

HOW TO PLEASE A MAN

When the woman's turn comes to pleasure her partner she should caress his body first before approaching the genitals. As he did with her, she then moves her hands gently up the inner thighs to the area around his testicles and penis, caressing the mons pubis, the perineum, and the anus. These are all sexually sensitive areas for most males.

The scrotum and testicles too are sensitive and should be handled with extreme care, though gentle kissing and sucking are usually exciting. Many men like to have the testicles carefully drawn into the mouth, caressed with the tongue, and then released. It is possible to tell how much the man is being stimulated by the erection of his penis. Stimulation that is too intense may bring him quickly to orgasm.

Whether or not he wishes this is his decision, for this is his pleasure period. If he wants to prolong the caring contact he may guide his partner's attentions to less sensitive parts of his body until his erection has receded slightly. Or he may wish to hold her quietly in his arms for a while.

This holding between periods of caressing is highly recommended. Without eliminating close physical contact, it reverses the habit of striving toward the goal of orgasm as soon as sexual excitement is experienced. Enjoying the stimulation itself then becomes the goal, so that all pressure for performance is eliminated. During an extended period of caring contact the man may partially lose and regain his erection several times.

The woman can help him regain it by caressing the penis itself, remembering that the shaft corresponds to her own labia minora and the head to the sensitive glans of her clitoris. The coronal ridge where the head joins the shaft is indented on the underside of the penis. The membrane of the shaft just below this indentation is called the frenulum and it is highly excitable. So much so that a few men don't like to have it touched. For most, however, gentle stimulation of the frenulum produces intense pleasure. The glans penis, too, is sensitive to caresses, especially from the lips and tongue, all of which contacts can be continued up and down the shaft.

If the caressing is manual, the woman will notice the enlargement of the penis as it erects, and the change of color brought about by the engorgement of blood. As her partner guides her hand she will also learn what kind of penile stroking gives him the most pleasure. This differs from man to man. Some like stimulation of the glans alone. Others prefer a gentle caressing of the underside of the penis near the frenulum. Most like a vigorous stroking, with the hand clasped around the shaft, back and forth from the base, over the coronal ridge, to the glans.

If the woman's stimulation is going to bring the man to orgasm, the testes will rise until they are pressed against the perineum and sometimes a few drops of fluid will escape from the mouth of the urethra. During orgasm, the pelvic muscles propel seminal fluid through the penile urethra under such pressure that the first two or three ejaculatory spurts may travel a foot or two if not contained. Later contractions are less forceful. Following ejaculation, the penis returns to its flaccid state and for a brief or extended period cannot be engorged again.

Manual stimulation to orgasm during caring caresses is an excellent way for intimate partners to learn and understand the excitation and response pattern of the other. Such understanding makes possible the richest and most satisfying kind of mutual sexual communication.

But oral contact with the genitals should not be neglected either. Many men are particularly excited when the intimate partner kisses, licks, and sucks the penile shaft, glans, and frenulum. Women who can't achieve orgasm through coitus, or have difficulty doing so, can often be brought to climax by the gentle, moist movement of the tongue in the clitoral area.

Since the lips and tongue are themselves erotic organs, most intimate partners who concentrate on the taste and texture of the other's genitals find they are receiving sensuous sensations as well as giving them. This mutuality can be increased by assuming the "sixty-nine" posture so that the mouth of each has access to the genitals of the other.

New Ways to New Pleasures

Even though the sexual pleasuring of caring contact has taken the demand for performance out of sexual play it may return whenever the couple attempts intercourse. Then the male has been culturally conditioned to think that *he* must decide when the female is ready for penetration, cover her as she lies supine on the bed, locate the vagina, and thrust until she has achieved orgasm. All these maneuvers add distracting handicaps and frustrations to the culmination of the sex act.

At a time when erotic pleasure should be escalating, the male finds himself presented with a double burden of responsibilities. The female finds herself pinned to the bed in a position that gives little freedom of movement and minimum stimulus to the clitoris. If she has not really been ready for penetration at the time her partner mounted, his forceful thrusting interferes with, rather than adds to, the compounding of sexual sensations necessary to bring her to orgasm.

At this point her own performance fears take over. She may try to will orgasm by thrusting forcefully herself. Or she may give up and fake. Neither solution is truly satisfying to either partner. And the memory of frustration and dissatisfaction lingers to add another quota of performance fear to the next sexual encounter.

There are several ways this sequence of events can be changed from a performance ordeal to the satisfying sexual experience it was meant to be. To do this the partners must discard the cultural assumption that because he is male the man is a sexual expert and knows what the woman needs and wants. And they must forget society's injunction that there is something superior about the woman-inferior coital position.

If both assume that the woman alone knows when she is ready for penetration the man can give up his feeling of responsibility on this score and concentrate on the pleasures of foreplay. The woman can give up her fears that stimulation will be discontinued too soon and let escalating pleasure carry her to the moment she desires intromission.

Then she should mount the male. This position gives her strong clitoral stimulation and allows her freedom of movement, so that with her partner she can share the pacing of the thrusting for maximum excitation of both.

With a little practice she can learn to mount her partner easily and effortlessly, remembering always that the penis is an extremely delicate organ. She should never try to sit on it. If she will put her knees on either side of the male nipple line, and grasp the penis with her hand, she will be able to slide back on it, guiding it effortlessly into the vagina. It is she who should do the guiding, for she knows where the vagina is.

Performance pressure is further reduced at this point if the male feels that he has given his penis to his partner for her enjoyment and if she feels that she has given him her vagina for his. Each is then responsible only for his or her own delight in this precious gift from the other.

Every sexual encounter, even with the same partner, is different. There will be times when both partners will wish a rapid escalation of sensation to quick orgasm. They will be missing a great deal, however, if they don't sometimes continue their absorption in the sensuous to the moments after penetration.

Holding the penile glans motionless in the muscled entrance of the vagina can be an erotic experience for both. Sensation can be varied and increased with slow undulating movements and with contractions and relaxations of the pubococcygeus muscles on the part of both partners. These muscles cause the vagina to grab and release the sensitive penile glans, and they can cause the glans to quiver against the vaginal nerve endings that surround it at the entrance of the vagina. This quivering can also be highly exciting to both partners if the woman slides off the penis and lets the glans vibrate against the vulva.

The teasing technique of mounting and dismounting, to lie together in a full body embrace, can prolong the pleasures of intercourse and is especially effective in escalating the excitement of the female. This is particularly so if the body embrace includes deep kissing and contact between the penis and the vulva. The feel of the penis, warm and moist from the vagina, in the clitoral area, is a highly arousing contact for most women.

Motionless, complete penetration of the vagina can also be sensuous for both partners. If the man can simply abandon himself to this pleasure, letting the female begin slow thrusting at her own pace, he can be swept along to sensations that are impossible when he takes command of coitus. Eventually his body's need for release will impel him to strong thrusting, but this is a natural, biological demand, not one he has imposed on himself.

After the partners have become familiar with the woman-superior position, they will want to try the lateral position. This placement allows maximum pelvic movement for both partners, provides body contact, and leaves each a hand free for caressing. It is so comfortable that after intercourse many couples fall asleep without changing the position.

In this position the male lies on his back, his legs apart, right leg straight, left leg bent at a 45° angle. The woman lies over him with her right leg between his legs and her left leg bent over his right thigh. Her left knee rests on the bed and her right thigh is supported by the inner thigh of his left leg.

A pillow should support their heads and another can be angled down beneath the woman's shoulder, for additional support if wanted. His left arm and her right arm can be circled under the pillows, or beneath the partner's neck, leaving one arm and hand free for each partner to hold and caress the other.

Once the partners have learned to assume the position, and are comfortable in it, they will be able to change from the female-superior posture to the lateral, even in the midst of intercourse, without expelling the penis from the vagina. For mutual sexual enjoyment this position is acknowledged to provide the most effective means of coital interaction.

Does all this seem a lot of learning to accomplish something that you used to think just came naturally? It does come naturally in societies where children and adolescents are allowed to fulfill their needs for intimacy and to express themselves sexually without guilt or shame. Doing so, through the years of growing up, they learn the sexual language of intimacy just as they learn their native spoken tongue. In our society intimacy has been discouraged. Learning it finally is like learning a foreign language.

We can pick it up on street corners and get by. Or we can learn it so well that we can understand its many nuances, use it for the most subtle communication, and perhaps even form it into poetry. The poetry of bodily communication is no less beautiful or worthwhile than the poetry of words.

10
Short Circuits

Your bioloops are paths within the nervous system which were meant to work automatically. Sometimes they are short-circuited. Sexual short circuits are most often the result of fear, guilt, pressure for performance, fatigue, and illness. Fortunately, our new understanding of bioloops usually permits us to repair the damage through learning based on awareness of bodily pressure changes.

The changes that your body undergoes with sexual excitation are all pressure changes. You can note them through your own senses, both within your body and by touching yourself. By using the muscles of your pelvic diaphragm, you can alter the pressure changes and increase your awareness of them. Noticing this pressure increase and decrease enables you to cause these changes to occur, not through accident but through relaxed acceptance and understanding.

Successful short-circuit correction demands an open-mindedness toward masturbation not only as a means of sexual relief but also as an important step in self sex education. Some individuals come into their full sexuality without any difficulty; others have to work at it. The way to start is through auto-manipulation of the genitals. You cannot expect a partner to fully arouse and excite you if you have no idea of your erotic potential. Nor can you expect to correct sexual difficulties without retraining your responses, partly through masturbation.

The Ejaculatory Short Circuit

The pressure bioloop for ejaculatory control was first used by call girls in Florida, with such therapeutic and financial success that it was soon adopted by ladies of pleasure in Manhattan.

Learning ejaculatory control depends on the sense of pressure that every man is aware of within himself: the pressure that announces an ejaculation is approaching. When this pressure is opposed by a greater pressure, applied by the fingers on the penis, the desire to ejaculate ceases. This pressure causes the muscles within the urethra to contract, sending signals that turn off the ejaculatory drive. This external pressure is a teaching technique that eventually causes a man to learn how to regulate these internal muscles without any external pressure.

When a man tends to ejaculate immediately after obtaining an erection, he can learn to control this through applying the bioloop method of pressure, quite firm pressure, on the penis as soon as erection has occurred. Part of this pressure should be on the frenulum. The frenulum is the bridle of skin on the underside of the penis just beneath the indentation where the glans and shaft join. The bridle is easy to find if circumcision has been done, and can be sensed in an uncircumcised penis.

Pressure is applied with one finger on the frenulum, and another directly above it on the glans just above the coronal ridge. The thumb presses the opposite side of the penile shaft just below the ridge. Rather strong pressure for a slow count of ten is needed. This pressure causes loss of the urge to ejaculate and also a loss of part of the erection. After fifteen to thirty seconds' rest, stimulation can be resumed to restore the erection. When the desire to ejaculate is again felt, a squeeze should be applied and kept up for another slow ten count until the desire to ejaculate vanishes. The finger pressure should be applied three or four times during the first sessions. Later alternate periods of stimulation and pressure control should be sustained without ejaculation for a period of fifteen to twenty minutes.

A man who has learned this ejaculatory control by himself frequently finds the difficulty returns when he is with a partner. By learning to apply finger pressure to his penis, the partner can help him gain control in this more arousing situation. To accomplish this, the man should lie down and spread his legs so that she can sit in a crouching pose below his penis. Or she may lean against the headboard of the bed, legs outstretched, while he, with his head at the opposite end of the bed, and knees bent over her legs, at either side of her body, gives her ready access to his penis.

When both are comfortable she should grasp his erect penis so that the ball of her thumb is directly on the frenulum, the thumb itself parallel with the shaft of the penis. Her first two fingers rest on the upper surface of the penis, one on either side of the coronal ridge so that they can press in opposition to the thumb. At first the man should indicate to her just when pressure is needed, and how much, by pressing on her fingers.

When they have been able to control his ejaculations for three days they should begin brinksmanship. Assuming the woman-superior position, the female partner grasps the penis and places the glans in her vagina. When he indicates that he needs pressure help for his bioloop she elevates her hips, grasps the penis and squeezes. She shouldn't do this too rapidly. After fifteen to twenty minutes of intromission, if he does not ejaculate, they are almost home free. But they should practice the squeeze technique for six to twelve months afterwards, and they must have regular sex.

The safety of this technique is assured from the many hundreds of times it has been used with no ill effects. It should not be used once ejaculation has begun, but rather at the point where pressure indicates ejaculation is imminent. It is considerably safer than the Tantric practice of blowing into the urethra, and teaches the same muscles the same thing.

The Orgasmic Bioloop

The first thing any woman who is having orgasmic difficulties should do is identify the sexual pleasures and displeasures that her partner gives her and talk them over with him. He should be willing to listen and take off the pressure for performance, even the pressure for coitus, while this short circuit is being repaired. Since he has much to gain from this, there should be no question about changing actions and attitudes.

In our culture many women cannot establish a regular orgasmic pattern without autoerotic training. This is best accomplished with a vibrator. Before beginning, it is well to do the preparatory thought loop for genital awareness. This concentration will heighten your bioloop, and increase the blood flow to the genitals.

Your thought loops should also contain pleasing sexual fantasies. These may already have occurred spontaneously as a result of other thought loops. Whether they have or not, you should make a very deliberate attempt to place yourself in a fantasy scene that is most pleasing and stimulating to you.

The training of our culture has successfully eliminated the ability of many women to engage in sexual fantasies. Women with orgasmic difficulties are often those who have suppressed this natural facility. If this has happened to you it is important that you re-learn how to fantasize sexually. To start fantasies you could try reading erotic passages in a book, or looking at pictures.

When your fantasizing has put you in a sexually receptive frame of mind you should use the vibrator. (To our knowledge nobody has as yet decorated her vibrator with sequins and called it "Harry." It's no substitute for an intimate relationship, just a help to achieving one.) A battery-powered vibrator is best since you can use it anywhere and there is no cord to hamper its movements. If you are investing in a vibrator choose one with two speeds and four rubber cups of varying sizes. Don't buy one that is penis-shaped, with the idea that it can be inserted into the vagina. Vaginal penetration will not teach you to have orgasms. You'll be using your vibrator in the clitoral area.

Lie on the floor in front of a full-length mirror. If necessary, use pillows under your hips to elevate your genitals so that you can see them in the mirror. You are going to teach yourself to respond freely to genital stimulation. Have a lubricating lotion handy and use it freely. Lie with legs apart, your knees up, and your feet placed firmly on the floor. Arch up your pelvis and hip area. Flutter your legs. Thrust with your pelvis and exercise those pubococcygeus muscles.

Experiment with the vibrator at different speeds. Concentrate on the sensations it gives you as you use it on the hairy mons, the outer lips and the inner lips of the vulva. Discover where it gives you most stimulation and enjoy it. Let your body express that enjoyment and increase it. Your first sessions should be at least thirty to forty minutes long, until you are experiencing several orgasms each session.

When sufficient stimulation is given to the area around the clitoris and accepted as pleasurable, orgasm results. Stimulation causes the vagina to lubricate, the labia and clitoris to fill with blood, and the muscles and nerves to do their pleasure giving. As the pleasure is savored, and stimulation continues, orgasm occurs. The heightened erotic state produced by the first orgasm makes the next one easier and each succeeding one more delightful. This bioloop runs an ever-charming circle until a fullness of satisfaction is reached.

To increase your sexual capacity you should also train your pubococcygeus muscles. This is easy to do when you are urinating. After you have passed a little urine contract these muscles to stop the flow, then restart the stream. With a little practice most women are able to do this several times during the course of urination. This will make you more aware and better able to control the muscle of your pelvic diaphragm. It will also help you at those times when urination must, for social or geographic reasons, be postponed. Some women find that they have a tendency to dampen themselves slightly in these situations, and this can be prevented by developing a strong pelvic diaphragm.

After you have become orgasmic with the vibrator you should practice reaching orgasm manually. This is more tiring, so if you are used to obtaining multiple orgasms with a vibrator you won't expect as many with the hand, but you will find out just what kind of manual manipulation stimulates you and where it is most effectively applied. This is information you will want to pass on to your partner so that he will be able to arouse you during foreplay. The way to do this is to let him bring you to orgasm manually under your directions.

If this idea embarrasses you, you may want to use the "back protected" position. In this position the man sits up in bed with his back resting against the headboard and his legs outstretched. The woman sits between his legs with her back "protected" by his chest. This gives her a feeling of privacy and security.

Using the techniques of caring contact he begins to caress her. He should caress her generally, then stroke her breasts, then her thighs, then her vulva, and back to the breasts again. He should keep this up for several minutes until his partner tells him by guiding his hand, not by talking, to concentrate more fully on her genitals. Even at that time she will find it more exciting if one hand continues to caress the other parts of her body while one strokes the genital area. She guides this hand by keeping hers on it so that her partner learns the kind of touch she desires and the places she prefers to be touched. Both should concentrate fully and completely on her sensual pleasure during this time. There should be no expression, spoken or not, about male desires and male needs.

This kind of foreplay should precede intercourse, until the build-up of erotic sensations causes the woman to desire intromission. Only she knows the proper moment. The man who enters too soon, and thrusts too vigorously, is only providing distraction, not satisfaction. The woman-superior position, or the lateral position, usually provide greater stimulation for the woman since she can control thrusting with a cooperative partner. A number of women like a modification of the man-on-top position in which the woman keeps her legs together, rather than spread apart. This enhances her labial stimulation and may be less mentally threatening than a position in which she is totally open.

The feminine sexual bioloop depends on a build-up of sensuous stimuli. It can be broken by performance demands. He says, "Haven't you come yet, baby?" She fakes it, or she tries to will an orgasm. This turns on the alarm system. Both of them have short-circuited. If instead they relax, and yield to the enjoyment of sensations, this turns off the alarm, and turns on loving, peaceful parasympathetic connections. This is the road of intimacy—the cure for short circuits.

The Non-Ejaculatory Bioloop

The cultural barriers that are the main source of woman's inability to become orgasmic are productive of a similar problem for men. Some males are unable to ejaculate within the vagina. They do not often come to a physician's attention, because of their misunderstanding of sexuality. They often feel that their ability to prolong intercourse for hours indicates a vast superiority.

Most frequently it is the woman who comes to seek help because she is physically distressed and emotionally distraught. The night before has been like so many others, two hours of active thrusting by him, possibly a multitude of orgasms for her, but ejaculation, never! Frequently the story adds the detail that after this award-winning sexual performance the man has gone into the bathroom and masturbated in order to have an orgasm. His partner feels tremendously upset. She fears she has failed as a woman. And she has been denied motherhood. She also suffers a very real physical irritation as a result of the sexual marathons. Nothing more dramatic than a sitz bath is needed to clear that up. What is needed for the larger problem is the understanding, education, and cooperation of her partner.

Usually his main problem has been an unwillingness to incorporate his partner into his sensual pleasure. He often obtains his necessary sexual relief with an established pattern of masturbation. He must learn to have ejaculatory episodes with his partner's direct participation.

A most effective method is oral stimulation of the man by the woman, complete to swallowing the ejaculate. This will break the barrier of his resistance to giving her his fluids. No matter how clean, pure, and low in calories the male ejaculate is—and it is—some women cannot bear the thought of swallowing it. Other women, equally normal, like to do so.

Manual manipulation of the penis can be used by women who object to the oral method. When the man begins to ejaculate the woman should quickly slip his penis into her vagina. Even if only a small amount of his ejaculate goes into the vagina the first few times, the short circuit is being repaired.

After the man becomes used to ejaculating within the vagina intromission can be tried *before* he begins to ejaculate, using the woman-superior position. The female partner should mount after she has effectively begun manual stimulation, and thrust strongly and demandingly. If he does not ejaculate after a few moments she can begin manual manipulation again, and, as tension rises, she can again mount and resume active pelvic thrusting. This bioloop, of ejaculatory release, is the reverse of ejaculatory control, and it can be repaired only with the help of a very understanding and cooperative partner. The man in such a situation has every reason to be deeply loving of his companion.

What has happened is that almost involuntary and usually unconscious contractions, or spasms, of the muscles of the prostatic urethra have turned off the ejaculatory desire each time it has occurred. Not surprisingly, once this bioloop fault is corrected, it swings, like a pendulum, in the other direction to premature ejaculation. This is easily corrected with the squeeze technique.

The Potency Bioloop

All males experience an occasional inability to have an erection. This is a bioloop short circuit caused by fear, often the fear of aging. Because of the fear and perhaps a sudden feeling of unworthiness, the alarm button has been pressed. The sympathetic system has gotten all charged up, pouring its chemicals into the bloodstream and stopping the parasympathetic. Usually it's a *performance* demand that sets off the alarm. One too many drinks, or several too many meals, can be the reason for the failure. It is certainly not a permanent condition, but rather an expression of a momentary inability. A common cold, with or without a slight temperature, can be quite enough to cut the bioloop circuit. Once the alarm is turned off, fear recedes into the background and success is automatic, if not instantaneous.

Reassurance from this fearsome worry can frequently be gained if a man will take time to reflect over his past erections. He will realize that when there is no pressure for performance, nor likelihood of being involved in sexual activity, he has erections. Quite often, first thing in the morning upon arising. Nearly always when he is asleep, and perhaps when sitting on the commuter bus or train.

No man can will an erection through direct, strained, and conscious thought. His mental processes are those of fear, which stop bioloop circuits. But he can gain an erection by relaxation. Some men are in too much of a panic to relax and allow the thought loops and bioloop realization. They need the help of a partner to restore their circuits. First, the man himself must put aside all performance goals.

He and his partner should begin with thought-loop concentration and caring caresses, with absolutely no demands for coitus or ejaculation for some days—even though he achieves erection. There will be other erections in the future. Nor should they measure the erection. As they continue to play together sexually the penis will increase its rigidity and size. This is an initial step away from the role that both have been playing, that of spectator. This has produced the bioloop shortcircuit that has stopped the enjoyment of sexual pleasure. During this time the man will learn that he can satisfy his partner without an erection, manually, orally, and even with his penis. It does not have to be hard to be good.

The woman can show him this by using his penis to stimulate her vulva until she reaches orgasm. She can also play manually and orally with the penis while stroking her partner's inner thighs and testicles. He should concentrate only on the erotic pleasure she is giving him.

When her manipulations induce an erection they may also cause fear that the erection will be lost before it can be used. The way to fight this fear is to let the worst happen. She should stop the play and let the erection subside, then bring it back again for her partner. This should be repeated many times until the male gains confidence. Until he can, indeed, respond with a full erection through erotic arousal.

The pressure changes that a man notices during his erection are no different from those a woman notices when she is erotically aroused. When his partner has been causative of these changes the man begins to become aware of the bioloop within him that regulates these changes. As he relaxes and enjoys the sensuous feelings, they increase. His parasympathetic sends his sexual organs the messages to hold blood, become larger, prepare for pleasure. These pleasure messages produce an erection.

It will be a big temptation, and a big mistake, if he tries too soon to use the erection to reach the goal of orgasm. That is really forcing another short circuit. He is trying to learn a new bioloop and he will do this best by forgetting any goals and concentrating on the sensuous present, and the pleasures his loving partner is giving him.

When the woman sees that her partner is achieving satisfactory erections regularly she can assume the female-superior position and place the glans of the penis in her vagina, letting the male partner enjoy the sensation without demand. She can increase the sensation by rhythmically tightening and relaxing her pubococcygeus muscles. Then she should dismount and they can lie together quietly, his penis between the lips of her vulva.

Later she can introduce the full length of the penis into the vagina, just holding it there. Slow, nondemanding thrusting can follow this, but she should always dismount before the male has reached the point of orgasm and lie again in his arms. This is extremely important and should be repeated many times to break the short circuit caused by fear of failure, and reinforce the bioloop that associates erection with sexual pleasure rather than with a demand for performance.

There are mechanical and prescription-drug routes that can be used to overcome impotence. But all other "aids" are short circuits themselves in the long view, because with them sex remains a detached and impersonal function rather than a part of you and your relationship. Relaxing into sexual ecstasy gives more security for the future and more joy in the present. And helping your loved one overcome problems that have given both of you pain is one of the most satisfying pleasures an intimate partner can have.

11

Brief Encounters

Most of our encounters with others are brief encounters. Even when they are romantic or sexual we wear our masks and play our roles and our games. Men pursue romantic prey like hunters stalking deer, counting the "points" of the future trophy. While pretending to resist or evade, women set traps for the hunter. Out of such exploitive relationships true love is supposed to grow, and to endure three quarters of a lifetime.

The wonder is that sometimes it does. The pity is that everybody expects it to. Our whole society is based on a family that is created by a marriage that demands exclusive lifelong affectional rights in a spouse who was selected because she had such outstanding gams or he drove such a groovy car.

Though so much depends on the brief encounter that brings two lovers together, society has done little to facilitate this initial contact. When you want to meet the man or woman of your dreams you're strictly on your own, or in the hands of those who are less interested in your goal than in the money they can make from your wish to pursue it.

For a fee, matrimonial bureaus and computer dating services will introduce you to someone of proper age, height and religion. Or you can make your own selection at a dating bar or singles party, knowing that he or she may be out for a one-night stand while you're looking for a permanent relationship, or vice versa.

Eventually almost everybody looks for a permanent relationship. Despite the divorce rate, marriage is more popular than

ever. Less than 3 percent of the population remains single for a
lifetime. That means that most people embarking on a brief encounter are hoping it will be permanent. It also means that they
will be wearing their best masks, playing "for keeps" games, and
ignoring all the signals that should warn them that this meeting
was meant to be just a meeting. For most brief encounters are
no more than that.

Knowing this, it would seem to be wisest to accept the fact.
You are going to have many brief encounters but only one, or a
few, long-lasting relationships. Must your brief encounters be considered unfulfilling simply because they are brief? There is no
reason that they should, except that you have learned, and
everyone has learned, that "love" must last a lifetime. Otherwise
it is something much less noble.

But is it? Should it be? Surely if you are going to base a permanent alliance on a brief encounter you'll have a better chance
of contracting a satisfying long relationship if the original encounter explores the components that make up long-term love.

Wearing masks and playing games are poor substitutes for
honest communication. They leave people lonely. So do feeling-
less acts of sex between the pseudo-aggressive male and the
pseudo-submissive female. They provide physical satisfaction
but no emotional nourishment. "Sex removed from the positive
influence of the total personality can become boring, unstimulat-
ing, and possibly immaterial," warn Masters and Johnson.

Dr. Abraham Levitsky, who is on the board of the Gestalt Institute in Berkeley, California, sums up the observations of many
psychologists when he states that "people are starving psychologically for communication in depth." Starving in the midst of
plenty because they are afraid to take off their masks and reveal
themselves to others.

They fear that if they show their inadequacies and vulnerability someone will take advantage of them. And someone may.
But to avoid meaningful contacts because of this danger is as
self-defeating as never leaving home because one might be hurt
in a traffic accident.

Some of the starving also feel that they must wear masks and
play games because everybody else is doing it. But, in fact, any

game has to stop whenever one player refuses to continue playing. The woman who drops her feminine role as the chaste and chased and says to the man, "I like you," allows him to stop his game of wily pursuer of unwilling prey. The man who treats the woman as a person he would like to know, rather than as a sexual object he would like to use, gives her permission to drop her defenses and be herself.

Can we suddenly be this honest with others simply by deciding that we wish to be so? Possibly not. We've been trained to play games and have to learn to relate to each other without them. We even play games with ourselves, some of them destructive.

The Lonely Games

We sit home alone, and lonely, telling ourselves that the reason we do so is that there is no one out there worth meeting. What we are really doing is dishonestly projecting our fears about ourselves on the rest of the world. We avoid the company of others because we fear *we* aren't worthy.

To test this, tune in on the thought loops that constantly go around in your mind as you carry on the dialogue with yourself that each of us pursues in his head. What are you saying? "I'm a nice person. I like me."? Chances are you are berating yourself for real or imagined shortcomings. Telling yourself, "I'm too fat." Or too thin. Too lazy. Or too ugly. Or sexually scared. Or inept. Or a social dud.

Trace the accusations back and you'll probably find that you learned them as a child from parents or teachers and that they aren't really accurate, updated assessments of yourself. All they really tell about you is that you've developed the habit of criticizing people, yourself included, instead of accepting them as fallible beings and appreciating and enjoying their Brownie points.

You can't truly know others (or yourself) if you are judging instead of getting acquainted. The best place to stop censuring, and start honoring, is with yourself. During your thought-loop sessions, several times a day, say "I like myself" over and over. Once that seed is planted in your subconscious you will notice a difference, not only in the way you feel about yourself but also in the way you react to others. The difference will be evident even in the way you stand and walk.

People who don't like themselves literally crawl into their shells, like turtles, when they go about. Their shoulders are hunched defensively over their chests, their heads are down, and their steps are either heavy or uncertain. Their bodies shout what they aren't admitting: "I don't like me. I'm afraid you won't like me either. So let's avoid contact."

Since others tend to value you as you value yourself, they *do* avoid contact. Or react with indifference, or hostility, when contact is inevitable. So, for the person with a low opinion of himself, all the world seems unfriendly.

But let him polish up his self-image and a miraculous change takes place. Now he moves with a relaxed and confident stride, chest out, head up, his eyes alert and interested in everything and everyone he sees. Part of his relaxation and openness to others is the smile on his face. It takes only fifteen muscles to form a smile, compared to forty-seven needed to produce the frown that most people wear when going about their daily business. Moreover, the smile is the human's most important signal of friendship, with no counterpart in the rest of the animal kingdom.

A person with a confident stride and a friendly smile tells others, silently, that he likes himself and wants to like them. And they respond by liking him. So the world becomes a friendly place, not because it has changed but because he has.

He has removed his mask of disinterest, or preoccupation, or his attitude that "I'm too busy and important to notice you," or "I'm too insignificant; please don't pay attention to me." And he has stopped playing games such as, "I'll be Rude Before You're Rude" or "I'm Here to Impress You" or "You'll Do Until Someone Better Comes Along." Having given up his masks and his games he is ready for intimate relationships.

And since he is ready he'll stop avoiding places where they can be found. For this is another way we protect ourselves from disappointment and possible rejection. We stay away from the spots where we might encounter either—which are also the places where we're most likely to encounter people who could mean something to us.

Men lunch at the club, with other men. Then they join the boys for drinks after work in bars that exclude, or discourage, women. And they spend the evening playing poker, or bowling, or watching the fights or a hockey game. Women lunch with each other in tea rooms, have their cocktails in cocktail lounges, and invite each other over for dinner and an evening of bridge or conversation.

Later these men and women may meet in a crowded dating bar, but since none of them has had much practice getting acquainted with the opposite sex they don't hit it off. They leave complaining that it is impossible to meet anybody with whom one could ever be compatible.

Because we have been taught to believe in the one and only love that lasts a lifetime, we devalue contacts that don't seem to have that potential. We miss the rewards of the brief encounter because we're not really there with the person we've met. We're busy comparing him with other possible mates, real or fantasied. Or we're projecting the relationship into the future. Will he or won't he lose his hair, earn enough for a house in the suburbs and two cars, get along with Aunt Bea? Will she or won't she get fat, nag, run up bills?

We presume we can make all these judgments at a first meeting, which means we're usually disappointed. Either we judge the person lacking at once or find out later that the relationship is lacking. Often the lack is a lack of contact in the here and now. If one or both persons are projecting into the future, then doubts and fears are ever present and defenses are never abandoned.

All this could be avoided if we understood that love isn't a miracle that happens in a blinding second. That something *does* happen—instant rapport, the chemistry of sexual attraction, or just a feeling of ease with each other—should be miracle enough without trying to make it into more. Love can be built of such small miracles if you take the pressure off and let it happen.

The principles of caring contact apply socially too. The first meeting with a new friend can be exciting and rewarding in and of itself if you accept it as a coming together that bridges the loneliness of two isolated individuals for a few hours. If each of you really attends to the other during that brief time, listens, and watches, and tries to understand and know, then a second meeting will have that solid foundation to build on, and a third should bring you even closer.

If there is no fourth meeting, even if there is no second—you have related honestly and fully to another human being. If you have not expected anything more than this, you have deeply relished the encounter. After that you *know,* even when you're alone, that there are people out there in the world for you. And that knowledge can eliminate the despair of loneliness.

And if, indeed, your brief encounter was meant to flower into a lasting love, it will become one without your forcing. Flowers, children, and love grow best with tender care that promotes but doesn't interfere with their natural development.

Getting Together

People are looking for exciting companions today, the pollsters find. And they tend to fall in love with someone who shares their interests. That is, skiers fall for skiers. Art lovers fall for other art lovers, or for artists. And those who spend their summers working on Indian reservations fall for those who are similarly dedicated.

It's easier for people with an enthusiasm in common to make initial contact. They have something to talk about besides the weather. This allows them to draw closer together physically, and this, in turn, permits them to talk more intimately.

That's because everybody walks around in an invisible body bubble of space that he counts as his. Reserved Americans need a bubble about two feet in diameter in order to feel comfortable. More demonstrative people, from the cultures around the Mediterranean, make do with a bubble a foot in diameter. That's why these people often call Americans standoffish, while Americans feel that they are pushy.

When you first meet someone, and talk about the weather, you can't get closer to him with your body than you have in your conversation. If you try, he'll move back, protecting his body bubble from your invasion. Nor are you allowed to puncture his bubble by staring at him too long.

A man often makes this mistake when trying to establish instant intimacy with a woman. He looks too long or moves in too close. And though she doesn't know why this annoys her, and puts her on guard, it does. If he had known the rules of body language he would have stayed outside her body bubble until she invited him in—by touching him as she gestured, or by staring at him a little too long.

Just as we learn verbal language as we grow up, so we learn body language. As adults searching for intimate partners we make mistakes because much of the body language we learned was meant to ward off intimacy. The adolescent boy is taught to keep "hands off" the good girl who lives next door. The good girl is taught to keep her skirts pulled down, and her legs crossed, and not to flirt with strangers.

For good measure she crosses her arms too, which is such a defensive posture that strangers don't flirt with her. As for the well-brought-up little boy, grown up, he learns that with his hands-off policy he gets no place with good girls or bad. He muffs it by making no move at all or by moving in too fast and getting his face slapped. Sometimes he doesn't even know why.

One student of body language, and of himself, decided that his early training had handicapped him so severely that he might never make the body language courting steps with any sort of finesse. So he took up palmistry. He has been a successful suitor ever since. He doesn't have to decide when it's safe to touch the girl. He just discusses heart lines and Venus mounds until she is impelled to give him her hand so that he can read her palm. After that they are on a touching basis.

Of course, such techniques, and many others, can be used by women as well. And should be. Because of their social training, women usually find it easier to learn and practice body language. Many of them hesitate to put their expertise to use because they've been taught that only "fast" girls flirt. And research has shown that about half the single women in the United States even today not only don't want to be considered fast, they wish to remain virgins until they marry.

Ladies' Choice

A desire for sexual innocence shouldn't keep women from selecting the men they want to meet and arranging to meet and fascinate them. Men just naturally gravitate to women who look receptive, friendly, and interested in *them*. The woman who can, with a look and a smile, send a wordless message across a room that says, "I find you attractive and would like to know you better," has an edge on every other woman around.

If this is the meeting that is going to develop into a marriage, researchers say that it has a better chance of being a happy marriage if the woman has chosen the man. That's because she's less apt to make her selection on physical attributes alone. Somewhere deep in her consciousness is the realization that this man might be the father of her children and she judges him accordingly.

If she wishes to remain a virgin until marriage she can make him aware of her feelings early in their acquaintanceship. Men still dream of marrying a virgin bride. And a little patience isn't a bad attribute for any man to have if he is looking for an intimate relationship. Despite the new sexual freedom, and the recognition that women are sexual beings too, relatively few women indulge in sex for sex's sake. Even the woman who doesn't wait for marriage to sanction physical intimacy is likely to wait for love.

The difference between her and her not-until-marriage sister seems to be that she doesn't necessarily expect her first love to last. She believes that love can come more than once and agrees with the experts that in marriage "when" is as important as "who." She herself often decides that she and her lover aren't ready for marital responsibilities.

But even when he leaves her it doesn't shatter her self-esteem. Nor does she consider herself damaged merchandise. More often she feels the relationship was enhancing, researchers have found, and she doesn't regret it. Researchers also find that the marriages of women who have had premarital sexual experience are reportedly happier than other marriages. They also find that half the women who have never experienced orgasm before the wedding fail to achieve it in the first year of marriage.

The end of an affair can be an unhappy time, but it is usually less so if the lovers have been emotionally as well as physically intimate. Then there has been enough honesty that they have always faced realistically the possibility that the relationship might not last. And there is enough empathy that they can take leave of each other without inflicting unnecessary injury. More important, both retain the personal growth that a creative alliance fosters. And this allows them to proceed to other relationships with self-confidence and realistic expectations.

12

Swapping and Swinging

Living happily ever after happens more often in stories than in real life. One third of the couples who vow to love a lifetime eventually renounce the vows legally and return to the singles world to search for new mates. Surveys indicate that many of those who remain married stay together for reasons other than love. One study found that only half their sample of married couples was happy after seven years. Seven years after that they too were disillusioned. Twenty-one years of marriage, for the entire population, is a peak time for divorce.

Infidelity is often used as an index of marital dissatisfaction. A quarter of a century ago Kinsey and his associates found that by the age of forty-four more than 50 percent of husbands and 25 percent of wives had been unfaithful. Most observers feel the numbers have risen since then.

Not an irresistible new love outside the home but boredom within it is usually the reason mates stray. Boredom is also the reason many couples retire from sex at about the same time they retire from work. Variety in lovemaking places, positions, and times, recommended by the marriage manuals, hasn't kept ennui at bay.

Divorce, infidelity, or boredom weren't the alternatives most couples envisioned at the altar. They dreamed of an intimacy in which each would fulfill all the needs of the other for a lifetime. Quite possibly this is an unrealistic expectation, but it is also part of our culture. When marriage fails to meet all our sexual and intimacy needs we blame ourselves and our partners rather than the impossible dream. Blaming the partner gives one spouse an excuse for seeking beyond the marriage the satisfactions he hasn't found within it. He rarely finds them on the outside either.

Extramarital affairs involve lying, hiding, and deception, none of which foster intimacy either within the marriage or in the other relationship. Since the extramarital affair is usually undertaken in a search for intimacy, this is a disappointment to the partner who strays.

"We might have had something but I couldn't keep up the double life," psychiatrists hear constantly. From the betrayed partner they hear, "I could forgive the infidelity but not the lying and deception."

Is there a way to separate the two? Increasing numbers of couples think so. An estimated ten million of them practice open infidelity in the presence of their mates and with the full knowledge, consent, and cooperation of the marital partner. They are known as swingers, or mate swappers.

Most swingers tell researchers that they began swinging when their marriages were foundering and that the experience has improved their relationship and their marital lovemaking. They chose swinging instead of extramarital affairs because they feared that these would undermine the marriage.

With swinging there is no lying and no deception. The couple is still a marital unit when they exchange sexual favors with the members of another marital unit. And they go to swinging parties together. Neither contacts another swinger without the knowledge and consent of the spouse. This is a safeguard against an outside emotional entanglement that might threaten the marriage.

Fifteen years ago the swinging scene was confined to a few couples in a few suburbs. It has since grown into big business. Fifty magazines, published by fifty swingers' clubs across the country, carry as many as 3,500 advertisements an issue, placed by swinging couples wanting to meet others similarly inclined. Other advertisements of the same kind appear in the underground press. Swingers' bars or cocktail lounges cater to swinging couples and give them a place to meet and get acquainted. Organizations keep files of swingers so that compatible couples can be introduced to each other. They also arrange and sponsor swinging parties.

Not all swingers are married, though the rules of some clubs insist that members must be. Almost all parties exclude people without partners. Some clubs maintain lists of unattached swingers so that one without a partner, either for a party or a lonely night, will be able to get in touch quickly with another. Even in clubs that are for "marrieds only," about one-third of the participants are couples who are only posing as married.

The sexual parties of swinging clubs differ only in minor details. Most are held in private homes. Alcohol is almost always served and disrobing is usually delayed until drinking has dissolved inhibitions. Marijuana is more often forbidden, mostly because it is against the law.

Occasionally a pornographic film is shown as an ice breaker. And if the party doesn't get off the ground, the host and hostess may start a game. A popular one is squirting everybody with whipped cream, which participants then lick from each other's bodies. More often music and dancing, in the nude, inspire the guests to sexual activities.

The rule is, always, that nobody has to do anything he doesn't want to do. No one forces his attentions on anyone else. Anyone who wishes to can watch instead of participating and many couples do, at least during their first few parties.

Some couples always remain voyeurs. They go to parties because watching the sexual activities turns them on for their own lovemaking, which they prefer to confine to the privacy of their own homes. They say they also learn new sexual techniques by watching the activities at the parties.

Bolder party goers take part in group sex activities, such as daisy chains. Though every kind of sexual activity can be fitted into the daisy chain, and frequently is, it is usually started by oral enthusiasts, who carry out an extension of the sixty-nine posture that could, theoretically, run to infinity. Others retire to bedrooms in pairs or threesomes. Privacy, even there, is still usually minimal, with several couples sharing a bed and others waiting and watching.

As sex researchers have found in laboratories, people easily shed their need for privacy during sexual play. Strangely, most swingers also successfully shed their jealousy. The consensual nature of swinging seems to be largely responsible. Researchers find that only about 27 percent of the males and 34 percent of the females report jealous reactions.

This small margin of augmented jealousy seems to be the only way in which the adjustment of females to swinging is below that of males. Though husbands usually initiate a couple's involvement in the swinging scene, it is the wife who reports the most satisfaction from the sexual encounters, particularly at parties.

The pressure for performance on the male during parties is intense. Sex therapists trace many sexual problems, particularly premature ejaculation, back to party participation. The men just can't perform up to their playboy expectation of themselves. Researcher Gilbert D. Bartell, of Northern Illinois University, sees this as one of the most important negative aspects of the swinging scene.

It is a common male fantasy that he is surrounded by beautiful naked women and capable of satisfying each and every one. When he finds himself in this situation, however, anxiety takes over. And with it a negative bioloop. Seventy-five percent of swinging males interviewed by researchers report some performance troubles at parties and an envy of women who can remain sexually active throughout the night.

Whatever their reasons, men at parties often encourage their partners to engage in homosexual relations with other women. Bartell reports that 65 percent of the women say they enjoy these contacts. Very often, at the end of a party, the only people still swinging are women, satisfying each other. This acts as another blow to the male ego, particularly since homosexuality is frightening to most heterosexual men. Almost no homosexual activity takes place between males at swinging parties.

Because they face fewer performance tests in a simple exchange of partners, many men prefer mate swapping to the party scene and take their wives to parties and swingers' bars only to pick up congenial couples with whom they can swap. Other swingers ignore the party scene completely, finding its sexual freedom too mechanistic and impersonal to be satisfying. Many of these have their own neighborhood groups with whom they have swapped partners for years, in round-robin fashion. "We find it more fun than bridge," they say.

Society has looked no more kindly on the swinging scene than on any other deviation from the legal, lifelong, one man–one woman relationship. Swingers have been condemned as immoral, perverted, revolutionary, neurotic, and/or mentally ill. Without really investigating the swinging scene, critics have suggested both that these deficiencies cause swingers to swing and that swinging causes these deficiencies.

Who Are the Swingers?

Anthropologists, sociologists, and psychologists who have actually studied the phenomenon of swinging find that the usual labels just don't fit the labeled, either before, during, or after their participation in co-marital and group sexual activities. Most swingers are professional people of the upper middle class. Eighty percent have gone to college. Fifty percent have graduated, and thirty percent have pursued graduate studies. In every way but sexually they are quite conventional.

The married swingers have responsible positions. They own homes, cars, boats, rear children, attend PTA meetings. About half of them also attend church on Sunday. Many of those who don't, blame their religious upbringing for the sexual problems and inhibitions they have had to work through.

The majority of those who participate in mate swapping and group sex are recreational swingers, deeply committed both to the institution of marriage and to their own unions. They began to swing because they saw a lack of sexual variety as a threat to their marriages but disapproved of the adultery their neighbors practiced to alleviate boredom. They viewed the emotional entanglements of extramarital affairs as a threat to marriage. And they considered the deception necessary in carrying out such affairs disruptive of the trust and confidence that should be part of a marital relationship. Swinging was their solution. Their motto is, "The couple who swings together stays together."

The only deception they practice is one forced on them by society. Because of social disapproval and legal restrictions, they keep their sexual activities a secret. And because most of the married couples stand to lose both jobs and status if their secret is discovered, this can become a worrisome burden. Discretion is the rule. Only first names are used at parties. Exchanges are ordinarily made between couples of like circumstances so that each will have as much to lose should either be tempted to tattle on the other.

The need for secrecy on the part of many married swingers is the reason that singles are so often excluded from parties. They go, of course, anyway, with a partner who may be a steady boy friend or girl friend, or with a pickup for the evening. Sometimes single males pay prostitutes or call girls to accompany them to a party. When there is an outbreak of venereal disease in a group, this source is usually blamed. Very little VD has been reported among swingers, however.

Many of the single men who attend the parties say that they do so to look for sexually liberated girl friends. Many of the single girls are quite frankly looking for husbands with whom they will be sexually compatible. Both are often disappointed.

The idea that everybody who attends swinging parties is uninhibited and sexually available to everybody else is among the myths that have grown up around the little-known swingers' world. Numbers of people, couples as well as singles, join swinging groups because they recognize that they have inhibitions that interfere with full sexual expression. For them, the party acts as an aphrodisiac, but like an aphrodisiac its effect wears off eventually.

Researchers have found male virgins among the nonparticipants at parties. These men use the group sessions to learn sexual techniques and in the hopes that the excitement they experience as voyeurs will eventually overcome their fears so that they can participate.

Some women who are sexually active at parties can't bring themselves to be so in an intimate one-to-one relationship. Their upbringing has been so repressive that unless they see others engaging in sexual play they can't believe that it's a permissible activity. They also feel shielded by the anonymity of a large party and prefer to attend with men who know no more about them than their first names.

In this desire for anonymity they resemble the married couples with whom they mingle. Both are involved in swinging only as recreation. They aren't trying to change the world.

A small minority, known as Utopian swingers, *are* trying to change the status quo. They object to the legal and social restrictions that have been placed on sexual behavior and carry on a running battle for sexual freedom.

Most (though not all) of these Utopians are young people still in college or just recently out. Many are single and few have ever aspired to positions of economic importance or of status in the community. As other young people work for liberation of the blacks, the women, the Indians, the farmworkers, so these idealists work for the liberation of the sexual being. Their aim is to achieve a society in which human sexuality is accepted rather than denied, and in which consenting adults are free to seek sexual pleasure and fulfillment in any way they wish without interference from the state.

One of these Utopian groups was born in a blaze of publicity on a summer day in 1965 when a naked student from San Francisco State College, flanked by two girl friends in the buff, walked into the chilly waters of San Francisco Bay. The student's name was Jefferson Poland. He spent several weekends in jail as a result of his stunt and he also got front page coverage for his newly founded Sexual Freedom League.

He had been trying for some time to found the organization, first in New York and then in San Francisco, as a purely Utopian project. A fellow student suggested that people might be more interested in joining if they thought that they were going to get sexual action as well as social action. The friend was right. Less than six years later the organization had sixteen units across the country and several hundred members.

Most of the members are still more interested in the group sex available at League parties than in reforming society. But a hard core of leaders keeps them informed on social needs, injustices, and progress. For the most part these are the same leaders who placed the infant League in the forefront of the fight to permit coed dormitories on college campuses half a dozen years ago. That fight has been won, so they believe that progress can be made if it's just given a push. And they're pushing it.

In San Francisco they not only put on regular group sex parties but also workshops in massage and the production of pornographic pictures and movies. They conduct weekly adult sex-education discussion groups, and encounter and weekend sexual sensitivity sessions in which they claim to combine Esalen encounter techniques with sexual therapy on the lines taught by Masters and Johnson.

The San Francisco League includes gay members of both sexes, and served as a contact source for the mammoth study of homosexuality soon to be published by the Indiana Institute of Sex Research. The League also fights social and sexual discrimination against homosexuals and prostitutes. It is against abortion laws and also other laws that restrict sexual freedom. It is one of the parties that has filed civil suit to test California's laws against oral and anal sex.

Strongly in favor of pornography and against censorship, the League is currently making a movie of its own and other sub-rosa sexual activities in northern California. Deciding that sex and politics can't, or shouldn't, be separated, it came out against the war in Vietnam and in favor of the vote for eighteen-year-olds. Both stands brought cries of anguish from its conservative recreational-sex members.

League leaders, like many other Utopian swingers, are disappointed that the issue of sexual freedom hasn't attracted more political activists. They feel that the ecologists identify them as in favor of reproductive sex and that the women's liberation movement does not distinguish between their philosophy and that of *Playboy* magazine, which it considers sexist.

Jefferson Poland is a member of the National Organization For Women, and writes articles for publication against the double standard and in favor of equality for women. He has recently suggested changing the name of the League to the Sensual League to avoid confusion about its purposes.

With other Utopian swingers, League members, together and individually, are interested in alternatives to monogamous marriages. With others, many are studying and trying the possibilities.

Group Marriage

Group marriage, as defined by sociologists Larry and Joan Constantine, is "a voluntary association into a family group of three or more members, based on deep affective bond, genuine intimacy, and interpersonal commitments between all members." The marriage, including sexual relations for the adults, includes all members of the family.

Different groups handle their sexual commitments in different ways. One group may practice group sex, with all members participating together. Others allow a free choice of sexual partners with a change when desired. In other groups, partners are rotated on a fixed schedule.

In *Proposition 31*, author Robert Rimmer differentiates between swingers and participants in group marriages: "Wife swappers flee from involvement while we love it." The Constantines feel that this involvement cannot be sustained when a group becomes too large. Groups held together solely by the marriage itself rather than a communal activity of some kind rarely number more than ten, they find.

Many communes, much larger, also practice group marriage

with free interchange of partners but they are held together by other factors. Usually they have a religion or philosophy in common and very often a farm or business too. Their sexual partners also often share all the money and property.

Neither group marriage nor communes are recent innovations. Plato describes group marriage in *The Republic,* and communes have been a part of the American scene since 1680. Neither these older experiments, with unorthodox sexual union, nor the more recent mate swapping and group marriage arrangements appear, so far, to have undermined the institution of marriage. But such experiments with unions that do not demand permanent fidelity do show us that workable alternatives can be found to monogamous marriage and that they can exist along with it.

People come in many different varieties, and quite possibly they need a variety of sexual life styles to meet their different needs. Rather than attempting to pour everybody into monogamous molds, we might be better advised to approve alternatives that are not socially disruptive. If we don't we may force the dissatisfied to make choices that are socially destructive.

13

Seducing the Partner

Marriage, or a long-term intimate relationship, is as comfortable as an old pair of slippers. And should be. That is an important reason why two people form an intimate partnership. So that he doesn't always have to be Prince Charming. And she doesn't always have to be seductive.

Almost everybody feels lovable all dressed up and in good spirits. But the time we need love most is when we don't feel lovable. With a bad cold, an embarrassing blemish, short on funds, or without a job, we can't ask for affection from a stranger. We can from a spouse or a long-term intimate partner.

And that is when love means the most, because it is desperately needed for self-esteem. When you see couples who have been happily married for fifty years, don't believe for a minute that it happened because he shaved even on Sunday, or she never let him see her in curlers. It happened because they took each other over the rough spots, generously and gallantly. That is love. He may be a lazy good-for-nothing and she an addle-brain, and both be fifty pounds overweight, but if each has always been there for the other in the pinches, neither would exchange partners with the most glamorous couple in Hollywood.

Even at its worst, the marriage or the long-term relationship has a lot going for it, as many an extramarital mistress and lover have learned the hard way. Rarely do we positively weigh the pros and cons of taking a mate. More often the mate is subconsciously "imprinted" on us. Once that has happened no one else will do.

The Power of Imprinting

Imprinting is a common biological phenomenon. Newly hatched ducks are immediately imprinted by the first moving object they see. If this is an orange balloon, it is forever afterward "mother."

People are imprinted early in life too, by parents, older brothers and sisters, teachers, and other significant adults. Later we often fall in love with those who resemble this first imprinting. And they imprint in turn. Perceptive people recognize what is happening and go along with it or reason themselves out of it.

Richard Burton has said that he was "imprinted" by Elizabeth Taylor because she resembled a sister whom he had adored. A psychiatrist who refused to be imprinted analyzed his overwhelming attraction to a woman in an airplane and found that the coat she wore resembled a coat his mother had worn long years before.

Unfortunately intimate partners often ignore the power of imprinting. *He* fell for *her* because she was an independent career woman. She marries him and becomes a dependent housewife. Neither ever understands why both are disappointed.

Or *she* marries *him* because he is a happy-go-lucky sort. Then he begins to take his responsibilities seriously. He becomes a rising young executive instead of the fun-loving companion with whom she fell in love. Neither ever understands why they begin to turn each other off.

Couples who understand imprinting will take care to imprint with their true personalities. Unfortunately, in our society we are taught gender roles, whether or not they are appropriate to us individually. The woman learns to appear helpless, even when she isn't. The man learns to look masterful, even when he isn't. Both believe that unless they assume these stereotyped roles they will be rebuffed by the opposite sex. They are chagrined when their role playing breaks down in a crisis and upset when neither partner can sustain the role throughout a long association. They are fortunate when they have seen beneath the masks and have been imprinted by the real persons who dwell there.

There are probably no secrets, at least subconsciously, in a long union of intimate partners. One reason for this is because extrasensory perception operates in any close relationship. There is nothing physical or magical about this. Quite possibly, in the distant past, ESP and body language were our only means of communication before we acquired the ability to speak and language with which to express ourselves.

Sadly, most intimate couples don't realize that ESP plays a part in their relationship. She fakes orgasm and thinks he doesn't know. But it registers in his subconscious. He cheats when he's out of town, and thinks she doesn't know. But it registers in her subconscious. Then, when the conscious mind cross-examines the subconscious, all is out in the open.

In a brief affair, faking and fooling and deceiving may get by. In a long-term relationship they are much less apt to. Long-term intimate partners know each other's minds too well. Very often if he's on a business trip she knows, long before he calls, how the conference went. And he knows how things went at home.

Intimate partners can use this faculty to strengthen the relationship if they wish. And many do. Try it some time when you and your intimate partner are apart. Use your ESP waves instead of the telephone wires. Set aside a certain time for mutual concentration. Then send thought messages to each other, taking turns sending and receiving.

Don't try to do both at the same time. Different mental sets are necessary for each function. The sender must concentrate intently on the message he wishes to send. The receiver must be undistracted, relaxed, his mind cleared and open.

Experiments at Duke University, the University of Virginia, and other respected institutions both here and abroad have shown that clear messages can be sent from the mind of one person to the mind of another, even halfway around the world. Some people are better than others at sending and receiving, but the rapport between intimate partners should increase their potentialities, and practice can make the potentials real.

You don't have to be apart, of course, for mental telepathy to operate between you. Nor do you have to be consciously sending or receiving messages. Intimate partners often have the experience of being able to say what the other is thinking. That is, if they are really intimate.

The Importance of Priorities

Just because the long-term relationship is comfortable, many couples neglect it completely, putting their priorities elsewhere. The once-intimate partners grow apart instead of together. Then when the partner is needed, he is a stranger and the relationship that should have been comfortable and comforting is, instead, strained and unrewarding.

Dr. Joyce Brothers often reminds young mothers that their priorities lie with the husband, not with the children. That is sometimes hard to remember in the midst of diapers, playpens, and formulas. Husbands just aren't as demanding as babies, or even teenagers. Precisely because husbands aren't vocal about their wish for attention, wives must be alert to their unspoken desires. In middle life children are gone. That's one of the times a woman needs an intimate partner to help her adjust to this change. If she has ignored or neglected the man about the house she may find him ignoring her when she needs him most—or she may not find him about the house.

Men tend to switch their priorities from intimate partner to career, once their courting days are over. Not only do they spend all day in the office but they bring work home, in their briefcases or in their heads, and mull over it during the time they spend with their mates. Even the things they appear to do for their wives may be really for their jobs. The bigger and better house, the Christmas mink, the country club membership, are often prompted by business considerations rather than a desire to please the intimate partner.

The worst thing that happens once other priorities start to take precedence over the partner is that the partner is used to benefit *them*. This almost always involves some remodeling. The wife tries to refashion her husband into her idea of a model father. He attempts to make her into the kind of a wife he thinks a rising young executive should have. Then they are manipulating each other rather than relating.

It is a game in which there aren't any winners. If either resists the manipulations of the other, the manipulator sees this as a lack of love and reacts accordingly. Trying to meet the demands of a manipulator is just as disastrous. No matter what the partner's talents as an actor, he will not play a new role as easily or as well as he plays himself. And the manipulator will be satisfied with nothing but perfection. As he or she acquires the habit of regarding the partner critically, and as the partner loses his or her personality in the assigned role, all possibilities of intimacy between real persons are eliminated and imprinting is lost.

Among the finest gifts you can give a long-term partner is appreciation of himself as he is, plus the right to continue to be himself, and periodic reminders that he has first priority in your life. These will do more than flowers and dinners out, filmy nightgowns and exotic perfumes, to add zest to lovemaking.

Not that flowers, a night on the town together, and alluring clothing and scents aren't important. But too many long-term partners stop giving right there. Those may be gifts enough for a new love. Tried and tested loves deserve more. Both partners have invested a great deal in creating the long relationship and expect much of it. Loves that last are too rare to be treated stingily.

The slogan of many money-raising drives should be the slogan of intimate partners: "Give Generously." Can't afford to? You can't afford not to. Particularly since fantasies don't cost a cent. Yet for some reason intimate partners constantly rob each other of them.

Out for a drive, she wants to stop at a house signboarded "For Sale." He steps on the gas instead of stopping, reminding her that houses like that are way out of their league and always will be. If she's never going to live in such a house in actuality, then he might let her live in it in fantasy for an hour or so, as they wander through it. This generous gift would cost him nothing more than time.

Out walking, he heads for a marina to admire the boats, but every time he starts dreaming of one, she reminds him that they need a new washing machine, or braces for Junior's teeth, or that they are already in debt. If she were giving generously she would not only let him keep his dream of a boat but share it with him for the afternoon.

It's heartbreaking how few intimate couples give each other so much as the common courtesies they offer friends and even strangers. He gallantly helps other women in and out of cars and across streets but leaves his partner to manage children, bundles, and herself in awkward situations. She wouldn't go to the supermarket without putting on hose and a smile, and combing her hair. But she will go to bed in a torn nightgown, smothered in cold cream, prickly with curlers—and expecting love.

He would never call a hostess at a dinner party a lousy cook because the roast wasn't done to his liking. She would never fly into a rage at a guest because he was ten minutes late for dinner. He would never expect someone else to be his servant. She would never expect someone else to be her hatchet man.

Intimate partners who treat each other so inconsiderately find their daily discourtesy reflected in their lovemaking. Giving and receiving generously and gratefully takes practice. You can't withhold other satisfactions from your partner and expect to be able to give sexual pleasure graciously, or to have it accepted joyously.

Of Money and Sex

Sex and giving in other areas are so intricately related that therapists can usually tell a great deal about a couple's sex life just by learning how they handle money. Does one of them keep a tight grip on the purse strings, making the other beg for every dollar? That is such an obvious source of contention that one would imagine that a couple who wanted to keep their relationship running smoothly would decide, once and for all, how much he needed and how much she needed and dismiss the subject from their minds and their conversations.

And that's exactly what couples do. Unless they are involved in a power conflict with money and sex as the weapons. He withholds money from her to punish her for withholding sex. And she withholds sex to punish him for withholding money. Or vice versa. Or sometimes he insists on sex as compensation for her extravagances, in which she indulges to make him pay for sexual demands.

When decisions about spending really concern money most couples can come to an agreement without quarreling. They can decide how much to spend for a house, how much to save, and whether to buy a new car or take a trip to Europe. When they can't come to these agreements on large expenditures it indicates that the choices represent far more than money. He thinks of the trip as hers, and she thinks of the car as his, and neither wants to indulge the other in this lavish way.

More often the money arguments are about much smaller expenditures. Why does he always buy the most expensive Scotch? Why does she take taxis instead of taking the bus? One couple managed to stay mad at each other for almost a month over an argument that began because she wanted to send a letter to their son at camp by airmail and he insisted it should go by regular mail. The monetary difference was exactly four cents.

When arguments involve pennies or a few dollars, couples should examine them closely to find out what they are *really* about. The woman might find that her partner buys expensive Scotch in order to feel important. Then she can not only give him the gift of this small extravagance but find other ways, as well, to make him feel important.

He might see that her taxi rides are little luxuries she craves and needs. Then he can please her by not complaining of the cost of the taxis and by adding other inexpensive luxuries to her life.

And both might understand that a man who objects to an extra four cents postage on a letter to his child may be trying to say that he wants some of the attention his wife gives to their son. The woman who is seducing her partner can give him the generous gift of more attention instead of a month of wrath.

With such small but influential attitudes and actions long-term partners are repeatedly seduced—or alienated. Just as wrath and stinginess can weaken the ties that bind, so can neglect. He comes home every evening and gives her a chicken peck instead of a kiss. Then he buries himself in the newspaper until dinnertime. After dinner one of them may acknowledge the presence of the other with a puppydog pat on the arm before they turn their attention to the television set. At bedtime he may ask, as did the husband in Jean Kerr's play, *Mary, Mary,* "Are you in the mood or shall I take a sleeping pill?"

After years of this they look at each other one day and wonder what they are doing sitting across from each other at the same breakfast table. Balding and with a paunch, he doesn't resemble the trim young athlete who once imprinted her. Gray-haired and twenty pounds heavier, she looks nothing like the girl he once thought he couldn't live without.

Growing Older and Closer

Is this the inevitable consequence of growing old together? Not at all. This couple's problem is not age but distance. They've been living in the same house but they failed to keep in touch. Had they really looked, listened, and caressed each other through the years they would constantly have reinforced the original imprints with updated and stronger ones. Then after fifteen or fifty years each could have looked at the other with the deep recognition born of love and as accepting of the changes in the partner as of the changes in the self.

Fortunately, even a long-term relationship that is dying of neglect can often be rejuvenated. And it takes only one to start the healing process. Say psychologists Dr. and Mrs. Richard Klemer, "As one partner begins to recapture some of the enthusiastic joy in just being with the other, the other will gradually allow himself to lessen his own built-up ego defenses and begin to be more positively appreciative himself."

That doesn't mean demanding love and attention from the other, but rather giving generously of both. Body language and an openness to the other's thoughts and moods are generally more useful than words in reviving a relationship. The chicken peck kiss and puppydog pat are tokens of affection that dismiss the one to whom they are given. We use them with children when we want to say, "Run along and don't bother me." When we want to say, "I cherish you," to an intimate partner we need real kisses and lingering caresses. We need looking that sees beneath the surface and understanding that is all caring.

A couple whose body language and emotional rapport can't get them into bed without words are not going to speak very eloquently to each other in their physical embraces, no matter how many variations they employ in place, time, and positions. Partners who can kindle the spark of desire with a look and a touch will know when their intimacy needs the spice of variety and when it needs the comfort of familiarity. Both can renew the long-term relationship but only when lovemaking is the ultimate, not the only, expression of love.

14
The Intimacy Spiral

Intimacy isn't a static state in which a couple can dwell peacefully forever. It spirals up and down. When it's swinging upward the couple feels close, and warm, and secure, and happy together. When it starts a downward spin the partners feel pushed apart and helpless as their joy drifts away from them.

Sometimes they try to make up for their loss with alcohol or pot. When not used to excess, there is nothing wrong with either save that pot is illegal. But neither will shore up an ailing relationship. More often, they make things worse. For in the false glow of a drug-induced compatibility partners can ignore their deteriorating position. And while they are feeling temporarily better their liaison is growing steadily worse.

Then they start applying patches. The patches consist of flowers, and candy, and evenings out. They make love instead of watching the Late Show. He kisses her goodbye every morning and she greets him at the door every night. And still the intimacy spiral plummets downward. And will continue to do so until both the partners are willing to face the reason, and deal with it. That takes courage.

For a downward intimacy spiral begins when partners ignore feelings of anger with each other. The anger doesn't go away by itself. It grows inside each, feeding on new evidence that it is justified.

The Downward Spiral

Every morning and every night, when she has to replace the cap that he left off the toothpaste, her anger mounts. "If he really cared about me, he would be more considerate," she thinks. And then dismisses the thought, remembering the flowers and the lovemaking. For she's been taught that you can't love and hate the same person at the same time. And she wants to love him. Still, she gathers evidence of his lack of consideration. He doesn't even offer to stop by the grocery store on his way home from work.

He feels her anger, where once he felt love and acceptance. He notes that she doesn't bake the cake he likes anymore. When he mentions it she reminds him of the five pounds he has gained. For him this registers as rejection. So does the button missing from his shirt, the unpressed ties. He is resentful of her neglect. But what can he do? He doesn't want to start a fight.

But that's exactly what one of them should do. For nothing else will clear the air. The anger must be discharged or it will continue to contaminate love, no matter how many boxes of candy he brings her or how many martinis she mixes for him.

This fact is hard for intimate partners to accept. Each believes that he is "too nice" to harbor anger. And each is afraid that expressing anger will destroy the love they have for each other. Actually, not expressing it will be more destructive. For the longer it is nourished in secret the stronger it will grow, as each searches for new evidence that the other no longer cares.

She looks stunning when she's ready for a party. Instead of being proud of her attractiveness, as he once was, he reminds himself she never spends that much time and effort on her appearance when she is only going out with *him*. Is she looking for someone new? At the party he watches suspiciously each man to whom she talks, trying to ferret out his rival.

And she watches him, noting his sullenness and how much he

is drinking. And remembering that he didn't compliment her on the way she looked. Well, she'll show him that other men are impressed! And she proceeds to impress them.

To the surprise of both of them the explosion comes on the way home from the party. But by this time the fight is not about toothpaste caps and cake. It's about shameless flirting and shameful drunkenness. He rages and she screams, in a way they had always vowed they would never behave to each other. And suddenly, even in the midst of the battle, they are both feeling closer. He wipes away her tears, which have helped prove to him that she really does care after all. And she curls up in his arms, feeling warm and secure and close to him again.

For not only is each rid of his own anger, but in the emotional outburst each has touched the depth of his own love for the other and received a passionate demonstration that the love is returned. Not since courtship have they felt so carried away with feeling for each other.

A good fight can sometimes do that. Just as in dating days, there is the fear of loss. The uncertainty. How will it end? Each pursues the other. When one is sure of the other's continuing love he capitulates, making it easier for the "victor" to express positive emotions of affection again.

This can happen because hate, even though unrecognized, is a part of love from the very beginning. We are attracted to someone who has the traits we wish we had and before we take possession of those traits by loving the person, we envy and hate him for them. Just as hate isn't antithetical to love then, it isn't in opposition as long as love endures. That is, if it's recognized and properly handled.

Handling Hostility

Recognizing that one is capable of hostility is part of understanding and accepting the self. All of us—men and women—are naturally aggressive and naturally capable of hate. If these had not been part of our ancestors' natures we wouldn't be here. For aggression is necessary to reach a goal and that goal could be the preservation of life itself. Hostility is a natural reaction to interference with the drive to reach a goal. By sending emergency messages from the brain through the body it prepares us physically for greater effort.

That's one reason why it is so important that we express hostility when we feel it. Otherwise the body is kept constantly on the alert, with no relaxing relief and with all sorts of disabling consequences, from headaches to ulcers to high blood pressure.

It's helpful to be able to say, "I'm mad!" and then to do something about it. Sometimes all you can do is kick or pound a sofa or a bed. Or bat at a tennis ball, or knock a golf ball around the fairway, or hurl a bowling ball down the alley. These activities get rid of the extra fighting power our anger has generated in our bodies. But they don't put a faltering relationship on its feet again.

To do that you have to be able to say to your intimate partner, "I'm mad and ready to fight." But be sure you know why you're mad so you can communicate it to him honestly. Too often we explode with an anger which we haven't traced to its source. Then expressing this emotion can be destructive. A husband opens a bill and screams in rage, "I'm mad because you're the most extravagant woman in town. I should have known you would be. Your mother spoiled you rotten and drove your father to the poorhouse. Is that what you're trying to do to me? Well, I won't take it!"

He's getting rid of his hostilities, but in the process he's wounding his wife and chipping away at their marriage. Had he taken time to analyze why he was really angry he would be able to say, "I'm mad because you charged five hundred dollars worth of clothes at the dress shop when you know I am so worried about our finances that I haven't even bought a new overcoat, which I need much more than you need dresses."

With that statement he begins to rid himself of his anger and makes her aware of the reasons for it, without stripping her of dignity or undermining their relationship. Since he's being realistic he must understand that she will react to his anger. Perhaps with anger of her own. He must be willing to hear her out, as she has listened to him.

For if anger is to be used constructively the confrontation it provides between intimate partners will lead to greater understanding. And there can be no understanding if one does all the talking and the other all the listening. Or if one walks out while the other is talking.

There will be no understanding if she simply mutters, "I'm sorry. I guess I didn't think." Or, if she counterattacks with destructive hostility, or if she simply breaks down in tears and refuses to discuss the subject at all.

Neither can there be understanding if both are out to "win," explains Dr. George R. Bach, who teaches couples how to fight effectively. Winning isn't the purpose of a fight. And if one wins both stand to lose, for the one who wins usually does so at the expense of the relationship.

The most productive fights end in compromise. That means that each partner must give a little, or maybe one must give a lot. That means changing, for one or both. And changing is always hard. But that's what fighting is about. Fighting points up the necessity for change, and the direction change should take, to keep the partners and their partnership growing and vital. Change of that sort also switches the intimacy spiral from down to up.

Anger isn't always logical. It sometimes wells up from the subconscious unexpectedly and hits the wrong target. Recently, psychologists studying the wives of soldiers who had been in Vietnam discovered that this kind of anger was often part of the welcome home they gave their husbands. The women were distressed and chagrined at this, for they had been conscious only of immense gratitude that their husbands had returned safely, and of eagerness to see them. But subconsciously their loneliness had made them angry, and this emotion had surged up alongside the others when they were reunited with their loved ones.

Intimate partners often have to take the brunt of this kind of volcanic anger for which there seems no logical reason. It's one of the loving things they can do for each other. If a partner can view this kind of a psychological upset in the same light he would a stomach upset he can help his loved one through it, knowing that the other will recover if given time and patient care.

Coping with Jealousy

In a long relationship intimacy has many testing times. Separation is one. So is a period of too long and close association. Even lovers need time alone and breathing space. During periods of aloneness each person renews himself so that each has more to give the other when they come together again.

Possessive partners don't understand this. They cling too tightly and take any wish for independence on the part of the other as a rejection of love. In this way they often destroy the very thing they are trying to preserve.

Possessive partners are often jealous lovers. Whether the jealousy is warranted or not, the cure lies with the jealous person, not with the partner. For jealousy arises from feelings of inadequacy. The jealous one truly believes himself inferior to all rivals, real or imagined. He can only believe in his own worthiness if he has exclusive possession of the affections of the loved one. That's why jealous people are often jealous of children, parents, secretaries, bosses, even pets, as well as of romantic rivals.

A person who recognizes his own jealousy and wishes to rid himself of it can do so by building up his self-esteem and independence. Coping, meeting challenges, acquiring skills, are all esteem builders. So is an earnest effort to regard others as fellow human beings rather than as competitors.

Building self-esteem won't necessarily keep intimate partners from straying, but it is more likely to than is too much clinging. Improving the self-concept will prepare the person who is doing so to deal with infidelity effectively rather than spitefully. It will permit him to see the straying partner as a person rather than as a possession. He will be able to accept the reasons for the infidelity instead of casting blame either on himself or on the other. He may find that the other has needs that he and the relationship aren't filling.

That is no reflection, either on him or on the partner. Expecting one person to fulfill all the needs of another for a lifetime may be expecting too much. In that case some changes in the nature of the commitment or even a separation may be indicated. Or perhaps changes in the relationship can be made to meet the needs of the wandering partner. Or, to save the relationship, he might be willing to modify these requirements. In such situations there are choices, some of which offer creative solutions. But these can only be uncovered by partners who put the well-being of each person ahead of public opinion, duty, and punishment.

Crises in intimate relationships don't necessarily drive partners apart. Sometimes they draw them together. Illness, sorrow, financial reverses, can often open previously closed communication channels as intimates try to help each other through the bad times.

The Birth of a Child

Happy events don't necessarily strengthen an intimate relationship either. The birth of children, particularly the first, is a trying time in most marriages. And that can be true even if the prospective parents are very much in love and a child very much desired.

Both partners have emotional adjustments to make and the woman has to accommodate to physical changes as well. Even if she feels fine through her pregnancy, she constantly feels different and must keep adjusting to her changing body and body image. As pregnancy advances she worries about how her appearance is affecting her partner. Then, just as she feels most unattractive, sometimes as much as three months before she is to give birth, her doctor tells her to discontinue sex relations. And elects *her* to convey the message to her mate, who often doesn't understand the prohibition or doubts that it was the doctor who made it.

Chances are that the father-to-be has been worrying for some time that the baby would push him out of first place in his wife's life. He is also a little frightened about the responsibility the addition to the family will place on him. He has already been cutting down sex demands for fear intercourse might harm his partner or the child in some way. Now all sex is forbidden.

Many women give their husbands manual satisfaction during these months. Nevertheless, many husbands find a new sexual partner to accommodate them through the period. It's at this time that men are often unfaithful for the first time, and the extramarital liaisons they make are not always broken when their wives are sexually available again.

The moratorium on sex can last six months—three months before the birth and three months afterward. Research shows that this long prohibition is unnecessary in most cases. Infection is no more likely to occur in the last trimester of pregnancy than at any other time, and today we have antibiotics to clear it up quickly when it does occur.

There is no secure evidence that orgasm during pregnancy can trigger premature birth or harm the fetus in any way. Some women have gone into labor after orgasm in the ninth month, but more have had orgasms without triggering labor. There are a few women who, for various reasons, shouldn't have intercourse during the final weeks of pregnancy. But this seems an inadequate reason to deny sexual expression to all pregnant women and their husbands for several months at a truly crucial time in their relationship.

After birth, in most instances, if everything has gone normally, all obstacles to sexual intercourse are gone by the end of the third week. And it is then that many new mothers are particularly desirous of sex and of the love and attention of their husbands. Physical intimacy at this time could do much to bring husbands and wives together after a period of strain, and to strengthen the home into which the new child has been born. If physicians were also psychologists or family counselors, only the most imperative medical reason would prohibit intercourse at this time.

The separation of wife and husband during the birth of their child is also an unnecessary strain on the relationship, imposed for the convenience of the institution that is supposed to be serving the patient. Psychological researchers have found that women feel deserted and lonely during this separation, surrounded by indifferent strangers at a most important moment in their lives. Their husbands, also alone, suffer from fear, anxiety and guilt.

This separation can adversely affect the wife's regard for her husband, investigators have discovered. They compared the opinions of their spouses given by women whose husbands were at their side through labor with those who had gone through the experience alone. The women whose spouses had been with them viewed these men as strong, capable, and caring. The women whose husbands waited out the birth in the reception room or the bar described their mates as weak, frightened, and indifferent.

The Later Years

The period before the birth of the first child, when the married partners are alone together, is duplicated again some twenty to twenty-five years later. If, through the child-rearing years, they have given their relationship priority, they may delight in their new freedom and indulge in a long second honeymoon. If they have given all their attention to career or offspring, they may find that they have become strangers to each other.

Adjustments to the new togetherness are complicated by the climacteric, both hers and his. Today hers is better understood and possibly less troublesome than is his. For her, physical troubles have been sorted out from the psychological. Hormone replacement therapy can prevent or control physical discomfort, such as hot flashes and a thinning of the vaginal walls. And now that she knows that her sex life isn't over at menopause, and that her psychological problems will respond to a change in attitude and new interests, she tends to view the change in life with equanimity.

It is only recently that men have bowed to the overwhelming evidence that they too have a climacteric in the middle years. Most still insist that it's purely psychological. Nevertheless, when a physician sees a middle-aged male patient complaining of fatigue, lessened work effectiveness, and muscular weakness, he frequently finds he can clear up all these symptoms with tablets or injections of the male hormone, androgen.

He can't do anything about the middle-aged male panic at the thought that time is running out. This is as common in climacteric men, concluded psychiatrist Edmund Bergler, as measles are in children. The revolt against aging can take many different forms. The man may try to deny it by replacing his older wife with another young enough to be his daughter. Or he may give up family and career for sailing, beachcombing, or painting. Or he may give up everything, including health, in favor of settling once and for all into premature old age.

One of the panic buttons that triggers psychological problems in the middlescent male is the fear of permanent impotence. One erective failure and he is sure it will all be over soon. So he tries to cram enough sex to last him for the rest of his life into the years before some arbitrary cutoff date. Or he may try to ration sexual outlets to stretch an imagined limited number over a longer period of time.

We now know that aging isn't a cause of impotence. Some illnesses may cause it. More often it results from overeating, overdrinking, and lack of exercise. Nor is impotence permanent. Curing the illness, or instituting a physical fitness program can restore potency. Men in good health who have been sexually active all their lives can expect to remain so into their seventies, eighties or even nineties. So can women.

Just as good health in old age increases sexual capacity so does good sex increase good health. It is no accident that sexually active oldsters look and act younger than their contemporaries.

They *are* younger. Sex keeps their glands working. Because they have something to live for they walk with a more sprightly step, are more alert to their surroundings, and more eager for each new day. These are the rewards for those who have valued intimacy throughout life. Spending lavishly has made them ever richer. For them intimacy spirals upward in the golden years. Indeed, for all of us, if we will let it, intimacy can make all our years golden.

Your IPQ
(Intimacy Potential
Quotient)

15

Becoming — Questions

The three hundred questions in the chapters that follow were designed to measure your Intimacy Potential Quotient (IPQ). The questionnaire is divided into six sections, each containing fifty questions. As you answer each in turn, you will find your knowledge of yourself increasing. And you will become still more thoroughly acquainted with yourself as you read the "answer" chapters, which discuss the questions and the possible answers in detail.

To "know thyself" is a prerequisite for intimacy. For no one can be truly intimate with another until he knows himself well, and likes the person he is.

With this in mind it is important to remember that there are no right or wrong answers, as such, in this test. The questions are merely a means of surveying your background, experience, temperament, and attitudes as they relate to your intimacy potential. A high Intimacy Potential Quotient is not a guarantee of a happy love life, any more than a high IQ is a guarantee of academic success. Few people live up to either measure.

You *can* raise your intimacy behavior level and your Intimacy Potential Quotient, if you wish. You probably do wish to or you wouldn't be reading this book. Reading it, and carrying out its suggestions, may lift your IPQ dramatically. You won't *have* to test the difference by going through the questions twice, once before you read the book and once after, though you might find the difference in your scores interesting. Even *before* you take the IPQ test the second time you will *know* your IPQ is higher because you will feel so much more free, aware, and sensitive, not only to the experience of love but to all experience.

Unfortunately, you can't perform a similar miracle for anybody else. Each person must do that for himself, and he can do it only if he desires to change. You can't plead, argue, or cajole him into it. Such pressure usually builds even stronger and higher barriers against intimacy in his mind.

This happens all too often when two people of unequal IPQs are paired. Frustration on the part of the high-IPQ partner causes him to demand more intimacy from the other. The demand increases the lower-IPQ partner's resistance, which adds to the other's frustration. Both can become bitter and resentful, two emotions that are guaranteed to lower intimacy levels.

Intimacy flourishes only in an accepting atmosphere. This is best achieved by partners of similar IPQs, whether these be high or low. Such partners make no excessive demands on each other, which allows intimacy to grow naturally between them. Without effort, often without their even realizing the fact, their intimacy level rises slowly—sometimes, even swiftly.

If you want to have this kind of happy, growing relationship, you would be wise to learn the IPQ of your prospective partner or partners before you make any binding commitments. We have provided answer spaces so that they can take the IPQ test too.

Preferably, each person should fill in his own answers, with no assistance, guidance, or consultation. But if a partner is unwilling, or if you don't want to ask, you can fill in many of the answers for him/her. Once you've taken the test yourself you'll know what topics of conversation will induce your partner to provide the needed information.

You may want to fill in the questionnaire for your partner even if he/she is going to do so too, and then let him/her answer questions the way he/she thinks you would. Comparing each other's guesses with the actual answers will give you a clear picture of how well you really know each other. And this may increase intimacy through more perceptive understanding.

Knowing your IPQ, and that of prospective partners, should

help you to choose wisely. Certainly matching IPQ scores will be a great deal more helpful than basing choices on horoscopes, Venus mounds, or the reading of Tarot cards. For the IPQ tests will tell you about yourselves—what kind of people you are, how you think and feel, how you act and react. And they will give you a picture of how well you will relate in an intimate relationship.

Horoscopes will only tell where the stars were when you were born. And if that had anything to do with temperament and personality then everybody who was born in the same place at the same time would be alike. Horoscopes, fortune cookies, and tea leaves can be fun games to play. But not for keeps.

Of course you shouldn't base a romantic decision entirely on the results of the questionnaire either. It wasn't meant to eliminate the necessity of knowing your prospective partner well. It was meant to help you know him or her faster, better, and more thoroughly, so that any decision you make can have the firm and solid foundation that wise decisions must always have.

The questions in the questionnaire can be answered quickly with one mark. If your answer is "mostly Yes" place a + in the answer space after the question. If your answer is "mostly No" place a — in the answer space. If for any reason you can't answer the question, don't know the answer, or think that the question doesn't apply to you, place a 0 in the answer space. Use as few of these as possible.

For instance, you can answer questions that ask about your actual love and sex activities with a + or a — even if you have not as yet had these experiences. You've had them in fantasy and know (more accurately than you think) how you will act and react. Mark your answers accordingly. You can check them after you've had your real life experiences to discover how accurately you projected your responses.

You may wonder why some of these particular questions are included in a test that measures your intimacy potential. You'll find out in the discussion chapters. And you will find out, too, that almost everything has to do with intimacy. For your capacity for intimacy is, as well, a capacity for savoring all of life.

And now to the questionnaire.

Section 1: Childhood

This questionnaire has been set up so that up to three people can use it simultaneously. Each places a +, −, or 0 in the column he uses.

ANSWERS
+ + +
− − −
0   0   0

1. Was your birth an easy one? — — —

2. Were you a breast-fed baby? — — —

3. Were you often held, fondled, and played with lovingly? — — —

4. Were your parents calm and gentle about your toilet training? — — —

5. Were you a wanted child? — — —

6. When you were born were you the sex for which your parents had been hoping? — — —

7. Did you love your parents and did they love you? — — —

8. Were you brought up by your natural parents rather than by adoptive, or substitute parents? — — —

ANSWERS

+ + +
− − −
o o o

9. Did your family unit remain intact (no deaths or divorces) throughout your childhood? — — —

10. Did you have siblings of both sexes? — — —

11. Were you and your siblings fond of each other? — — —

12. Did your family eat most meals together? — — —

13. Did your family go on outings together? — — —

14. Did your family often laugh together, but not at each other? — — —

15. Did your friends feel welcome in your home? — — —

16. Were members of other religions, races and nationalities welcome in your home? — — —

17. Were your parents interested in the welfare of others outside the family circle? — — —

18. Did you have a grandparent, uncle or aunt of whom you were particularly fond? — — —

19. Did your household include at least one pet? — — —

20. Were childhood punishments verbal rather than physical? — — —

21. Was your childish idea of God one of a kindly and accepting creator of life rather than a punishing authority? — — —

22. Were your parents moderately religious, rather than fanatically religious or non-religious? — — —

23. Were your parents sexually faithful to each other? — — —

24. Were you proud of all the members of your household? — — —

25. Was your family in the same economic circumstances as the families of most of your associates, relatives, and neighbors? — — —

26. Did your parents refuse to listen to your troubles and triumphs? — — —

27. Did your parents criticize you more often than they praised you? — — —

28. Did your father refuse to help with cooking and housework? — — —

29. Was your father an authoritarian whom nobody dared cross? — — —

30. Was your mother a nagger? — — —

31. Did either your mother or father often say that the way the other parent acted was "just like a man" or "just like a woman"? — — —

ANSWERS

+ + +
— — —
o o o

32. Were the games you were allowed to play, and the toys you received, always those appropriate to your sex? — — —

33. Were you constantly reminded to behave "like a little man" or "like a little lady"? — — —

34. As a child did you refuse to play with peers of the opposite sex? — — —

35. Did you dream of marrying someone much nicer than the parent of the opposite sex? — — —

36. Were you jealous of the physical love between your parents? — — —

37. Were you ever reprimanded or punished for sexual curiosity, masturbation, or for playing sex games? — — —

38. Were you discouraged from watching animals copulate or give birth? — — —

39. Did sexual sensations in your genital area frighten you as a child? — — —

40. Were you more germ-conscious than your peers? — — —

41. Did you pick up most of your sexual information from your peers rather than from your parents? — — —

42. Were your parents evasive and embarrassed when you asked questions about sex? — — —

43. Did you overhear adults telling lurid tales about the dangers of childbirth or sexual intercourse? — — —

44. Did either parent ever tell you sex was a duty adults were expected to perform? — — —

45. As a child were you ever sexually attacked or seduced by an adult? — — —

46. Were all your friends of your sex? — — —

47. Did you only see your parents and/or siblings or peers, of both sexes, when they were clothed? — — —

48. Did your parents act more like strangers than lovers in your presence? — — —

49. Did you feel you were an unattractive child? — — —

50. Was your childhood mostly unhappy? — — —

This is the end of Section 1 of the questionnaire. Below is a space for your Childhood Intimacy Potential Quotient. You will need it to determine your final IPQ and to fill in the profile graph in Chapter 21. In increasing your potential for intimacy, or in improving a relationship, you will find these sectional scores most helpful.

To calculate your Childhood IPQ, count the pluses you have marked in answer to questions 1 through 25. Count the minuses with which you have answered questions 26 through 50. Add the two totals. Multiply the result by two. Count the number of zeros with which you have answered any of the fifty questions and subtract them from your multiplication result. The figure you now have is your Childhood IPQ. Enter it in the space provided below. Then move on to the questions in the next section of the questionnaire.

CHILDHOOD INTIMACY
POTENTIAL QUOTIENT _____

_____

_____

Section 2: Adolescence

This questionnaire has been set up so that up to three people can use it simultaneously. Each places a +, —, or o in the column he uses.

ANSWERS

	+	+	+
	—	—	—
	o	o	o

51. Did your family move often when you were a teenager?   — — —

52. Were your parents stricter than the parents of your friends?   — — —

53. Did you sneak out to go on dates?   — — —

54. Did the parent of the opposite sex invariably disapprove of your friends of the opposite sex?   — — —

55. As an adolescent were you suddenly rejected by an opposite-sex sibling to whom you had been close through childhood?   — — —

ANSWERS
+ + +
— — —
o o o

56. Did you mature physically either a great deal earlier, or later, than your friends? — — —

57. Were you worried that your penis or breasts were too small? — — —

58. Did you fear you weren't as "masculine" as other boys or, if female, as "feminine" as other girls? — — —

59. Did you, or anybody else, worry that you might be developing into a homosexual? — — —

60. Did you suffer a physical defect—such as virulent acne, or being too fat, thin, short, or tall—that was embarrassing to you? — — —

61. Did you go through school without being elected an officer of any group? — — —

62. Were you a "loner," with no close friends to whom you could confide your thoughts and feelings? — — —

63. Were all your relationships with the opposite sex romantic relationships? — — —

64. Did you spend all your vacations in the same way rather than planning and carrying out some adventurous summers? — — —

65. Did you drift through adolescence without any specific goals for the future? — — —

66. Did you explore philosophies and religions that differed from your own, such as Yoga, Zen Buddhism, Bahai, Communism?   — — —

67. Did you feel strongly about social issues and did you join your peers in social action?   — — —

68. Did you use drugs (i.e., alcohol, marijuana) moderately?   — — —

69. Did you drop out at any time to make the drug scene?   — — —

70. Were you in good health throughout your adolescence?   — — —

71. Did you welcome your first nocturnal emission, or menstrual period, as a sign that you were growing up?   — — —

72. Did you sometimes walk or run in the rain, wind and sun for the sheer bodily joy of it?   — — —

73. Did you often examine your developing body, including genitalia, with both eyes and hands?   — — —

74. Did you masturbate regularly?   — — —

75. Did you engage in mutual masturbation?   — — —

76. Did your teenage dreams and fantasies include sexual activity with the opposite sex?   — — —

77. Did you engage in masturbation and other sexual behavior without feeling guilty?   — — —

78. When masturbating did you feel that your body, rather than your hand, was giving you pleasure?   — — —

79. Did you read sex manuals and other "educational" sex material?   — — —

80. Did you read pornographic books and look at pornographic pictures, movies or live shows?   — — —

81. Did you usually fall in love with someone who reciprocated your affection?   — — —

82. Did you ignore warnings that physical intimacies with another might have an adverse effect on your moral character, reputation, athletic prowess, or health?   — — —

83. When kissing did you often feel sexual sensations in your genitals?   — — —

84. Did you pet on dates as a teenager?   — — —

85. Did you sometimes pet to climax?   — — —

86. Did you practice or permit "dry humping" in preference to petting?   — — —

87. Did you aspire to marry a virgin or to be a virgin at the time of your marriage?   — — —

ANSWERS
+ + +
— — —
o o o

88. Did you think girls who "went all the way" were immoral?

— — —

89. During petting or intercourse was your pleasure blunted by fear of detection or of pregnancy?

— — —

90. Were you ever exploited and then discarded by someone you loved, or did you ever treat another in this way?

— — —

91. Were you sexually promiscuous?

— — —

92. Did you at any time acquire a venereal disease?

— — —

93. Did you engage in intercourse without the protection of contraception?

— — —

94. Did you have, or were you responsible for, an illegitimate pregnancy?

— — —

95. Were you ever part of a gang bang or of a sexual encounter in which physical force was used to obtain sexual submission?

— — —

96. Was your first sexual partner sexually inexperienced?

— — —

97. Did you believe in a "one and only" love?

— — —

98. When in love did you and your loved one only make love, to the exclusion of sharing other activities?

— — —

ANSWERS

+ + +

— — —

o   o   o

99. Did you let lovers choose you rather than
   doing your own choosing and wooing?   __ __ __

100. Was your first sexual intercourse a sexual
    exercise rather than an expression of love?   __ __ __

Now for higher math again. To calculate your Adolescence
Intimacy Potential Quotient count the minuses in the answer
spaces of questions 51 through 65 and questions 86 through 100.
Count the pluses with which you have answered questions 66
through 85. Add the two totals and multiply the result by two.
Then subtract the number of zeros in this section's answer spaces.
The result is your

   ADOLESCENCE INTIMACY
   POTENTIAL QUOTIENT   ____
                                       ____
                                       ____

To better understand what the questions in the first two sections of the questionnaire reveal about your childhood and adolescence, read the discussion chapter that follows.

16

Becoming — Answers

Usually, when you take a test your answers are evaluated by an expert. In this case, *you* must be the expert, as well as the one tested. To help you understand the questions and what your answers revealed about you, we will discuss them in this chapter.

The discussion will be general, to encompass the wider implications of many of the questions. The questions covered by the explanation are identified by numbers at the end of the paragraphs that pertain to them.

1: Childhood

You may have had difficulty answering some of the questions asked in the childhood section of the questionnaire because you couldn't remember back that far. Not with your conscious mind, you couldn't. But your subconscious remembers.

It still clings to the self-image formed in those early years. In fact, many psychologists believe that the adult you are today was predetermined by what happened to you in the first five years of life, before you had much to say about it. Mostly before you even could talk.

This predetermination is pronounced in people who think that they were born with all their outstanding traits, values, attitudes, and behavior patterns, just as they were born with eyes of a certain color. And that, therefore, they can't make any changes. The person who understands that much of his personality was forced on him as an infant, by adults trying to please themselves, will realize that he can, and should, change whatever displeases him. Change will rarely be easy. But it won't even be possible for those who fail to appreciate how much infancy had to do with molding the adult.

INFANCY

The first question you answered in the childhood section of the questionnaire was: "Was your birth an easy one?" And perhaps you didn't know. If so, you were fortunate. Many people live all their lives with a feeling of guilt for the suffering they caused their mothers when they entered the world. They may also live with other, subconscious, feelings of anxiety and rejection left over from the birth experience. Psychiatrists have regressed patients back to that time, through hypnosis, and found the roots of many troubling problems there.

After all, birth can be a traumatic time for a baby as well as for a mother. He must struggle for survival, as he is propelled from a warm, known world to a cold and unaccepting one. Ashley Montagu suggests that it is at this time that we acquire an underlying tension that helps us cope thereafter with life's emergencies. However, it is possible, as well, to acquire from a frightened mother, herself tensed against the terror of the unknown, enough tension to be forever handicapped with anxiety and fear.

The baby who makes his birth journey to the reward of a mother's warm arms, and a reunion with her heartbeat as she nurses and holds him close, is well prepared for the next struggle. He feels that it too will be rewarded. But what of the baby stamped, numbered, braceleted, and whisked off to a bed and sugar water in the sterile hospital nursery? His first experience in his new world could hardly be called ideal. (1)

Unfortunately, despite the increasing popularity of natural childbirth and rooming-in services, this is the experience of most newborns in the United States today. They are received into the sterile impersonality of an institution rather than welcomed by a loving family. Half get no breast milk at all and most of those who are nursed are off the breast within a week or two. Bottle feeding is still in fashion, though this too is beginning to change.

Not only does bottle feeding deprive the infant nutritionally; it also deprives him emotionally. In the words of St. Louis researchers Dr. William Masters and Virginia Johnson of the Reproductive Research Foundation: "The infant 'learns' sexuality at his mother's breast, from the touch of her hand, the warmth of her body, the sound of her voice. . . . He learns the pleasure of sounds, of smells, of warmth, of embrace. And it is from this learning . . . . that his capacity for tenderness, for warmth, for love and sex is nurtured." (2)

Even the nursing infant may fail to learn these important lessons if his mother is fighting off the erotic sensations that often attend nursing. In that case the baby's instruction is quite the opposite. On the other hand, the bottle-fed baby may learn the pleasure of intimate contact if he is much loved and often held, fondled, and played with, by the mother and/or others. (3)

In many cultures children are allowed to toilet train themselves, in their own good time, and adults in these societies are not less continent than adults in ours, though they have fewer sexual problems. Our concern with early toilet training, and our rejection of the body's eliminations as unclean and unworthy, are taught to the child in diapers and remembered all too well by the sexual adult.

The toilet training anxieties carried into adulthood by the male were demonstrated recently by Anita I. Bell, M.D., of New York City; and Charles F. Stroebel, Ph.D., and Deborah D. Prior, B.A., R.N., both of Hartford, Connecticut. These researchers measured changes in the scrotal sac and testes, including elevation, in adult male subjects, in response to anxiety-producing questions. They found that scrotal changes were an excellent index of anxiety, particularly when the anxiety had been deeply repressed. And they found that in all subjects scrotal response of the greatest magnitude occurred when questions about bowel training were asked.

Dr. Bell, a psychoanalyst, explains that boys have difficulty with sphincter control because of retractions of the testes at the end of defecation. Because of this involuntary movement, arousing fear that the testes may be lost, boys are psychologically upset over bowel movements. Add to this the insistence of control by the parents, and very often punishment for failures, and the result is lifelong anxiety.

Little girls, too, carry into adulthood the adverse effects of harsh toilet training. Their struggle against enemas forced on them in childhood can result in involuntary muscular spasms that constrict not only the anus but also the vaginal opening and eventually occur spontaneously when entry into either orifice is attempted. The condition is called vaginismus and it makes coitus exceedingly painful and sometimes prevents intercourse entirely until corrected. (4)

If you couldn't answer the first four questions in the questionnaire in the affirmative, don't blame your parents. They too were the products of their upbringing. They did the best they could with the knowledge they had. The anti-intimacy chain isn't broken with blame but rather through a willingness to examine the heritage of childhood and use, with gratitude, those gifts that are enhancing while discarding the dross.

FAMILY

Research has shown that adults tend to reproduce in maturity the homes in which they grew up, even when these were homes in which they were intensely unhappy. Children from broken homes often find themselves repeating the pattern, despite firm resolutions not to put their children through their own painful childhood experiences. Offspring of alcoholics may marry, or become, alcoholics. Daughters of promiscuous mothers frequently become prostitutes.

For most of us, the pattern of repetition is less dramatic and, therefore, more difficult to see. If we can make it conscious we can pick and choose the parts of our childhood environment we want to recreate in adulthood and leave the rest behind.

Your training in intimacy got off to a good start if you were born to parents who wanted a baby of your sex, loved you dearly and taught you to return their love. A point off if you were brought up by substitute, or adoptive, parents. Though you may have been much loved, at some time you felt rejected by your natural parents even if you didn't admit it. A similar suspicion of rejection, and therefore of unworthiness, is common in children whose homes are broken by death or divorce. (5, 6, 7, 8, 9)

Training in intimacy is retarded for "only" children who have no siblings, as well as for those whose siblings are all of their sex. Which doesn't mean that just having brothers and sisters necessarily prepares one to relate well to a mate in later life. In a quarrelsome family, where nobody likes anybody else, the training can be completely negative. (10, 11)

A loving family shares activities, laughter, and fun, not only with each other but also with friends—including friends of the children. Its concern for people ranges beyond the family, and friendships aren't confined to people who are all of a kind. In such a family children learn that love levels barriers. It doesn't erect them. (12, 13, 14, 15, 16, 17)

A bonus in intimacy training if your family included relatives —not necessarily in the household—and if there were one or two related adults of whom you were especially fond. That's added security for a child and a prevention against his viewing all adults as parental figures. (18)

Another bonus if your household included a pet or two. Dr. Boris Levinson, professor of psychology at Yeshiva University, has found that children can relate to people with kindness and consideration if they have had the experience of caring for and relating to a pet. A pet also gives them a feeling of being close to nature. (19)

Just as intimacy can be taught, so can violence. And it often is taught by parents who believe that to spare the rod is to spoil the child. Children of these parents become violent themselves, or live life negatively in an attempt to avoid punishment. Or both.

For them everyone, even God, becomes a potential punisher. (20)

The idea of an Almighty who punishes those he has created, and despises the sexuality he has given them, is prevalent in our society. In treating sexual inadequacies therapists have often found their source in a strict religious background. Children who learn that God is love are better off than those who view him as a powerful tyrant. And possibly better off than those who, in their childhood, learn nothing of the altruistic love that religion at its best can teach. (21, 22)

A love like that can also be learned from nonreligious parents (Humanists, for instance), but the children may feel alienated from their contemporaries by a lack of familial religious belief. This feeling of alienation can also result from having parents or other family members who are "different," or don't live up to the community's moral standards, or of whom the child is ashamed. It can occur too because of economic circumstances, if one is either richer or poorer than one's neighbors or associates. Unfortunately these feelings of alienation can linger a lifetime. (23, 24, 25)

So can ideas of your own worth gathered in childhood from your parents' attitude toward you. If they were uninterested in your experiences, and rarely praised you, you learned to think that you weren't very important. And if the sex to which you belonged was constantly put down you perhaps decided you could never amount to anything. (26, 27)

Fathers give daughters this hopeless attitude by scorning women's work, treating the women in the family as servants, and assuming an authoritarian role. Mothers devalue sons by nagging and belittling the male parent. Both parents are guilty when they play up the faults of the other as inherent in the other's sex. (28, 29, 30, 31)

In their male subjects, researchers Bell, Stroebel, and Prior found that anxiety about male and female attributes was second only to anxiety about bowel training. It is probably as prevalent a concern among females. This despite the fact that researchers in the field can find no valid differences between the sexes that aren't related to reproduction. They do, however, find vast differences among normal individuals who are members of the same sex.

Still sex stereotyping continues. Dolls for girls and guns for boys. And parents worry not that their children will fail to develop their potentialities, but rather that they will fail to grow into "little men" and "little ladies." (32, 33)

Boys and girls struggling with sex-role conflicts, or who have given up their unique personalities for sex-role stereotypes, avoid the opposite sex as being beneath them, as long as society approves. Then, still playing a stereotyped part in the sex tragicomedy, they woo and wed, often unhappily. For actors playing sex roles are still only acting, no matter how well they have learned their parts. It takes real people, being themselves, to communicate and relate in true intimacy. (34)

If the parents are real people, relating to each other and their offspring as individuals, then they give their children an excellent marital model to strive toward. It's only natural for the daughter of such a union to want to marry her father and for the son to want "a girl just like the girl that married dear old Dad." However, it's a sign of an unhealthy relationship between parents and youngsters when children are jealous of the marital love their parents have for each other. It is then that unnatural ties to the parent of the opposite sex may interfere with later love relationships. (35, 36)

INTIMACY

In some societies children's playful and experimental preparation for their adult sexual expression is encouraged, and so they grow up unhampered by the shame and guilt that shrouds sexual activity in our culture. Parents who discourage, scold, and punish children for sexual curiosity or experimentation give them negative attitudes that are difficult to overcome. As a result the child experiencing erotic genital sensations that should be pleasurable may find them frightening instead and carry a mixed response into adulthood. (37, 38, 39)

Negative attitudes toward sex can be passed on from parents
to children in more subtle ways too. Stressing cleanliness to the
point that the child is distressed by human contact is sexually
crippling. Youngsters are also hampered if parents avoid the subject of sex, or are embarrassed by it, so that children must pick
up their information from playmates. Thus the children learn
that sex is so bad that nice people don't even mention it. They
also pick up a lot of misinformation. Fear and apprehension
mount if they overhear adults telling lurid tales about the consequences of sex and learn, as well, that this dreadful activity will
one day be one of their duties as a man or a woman. (40, 41, 42,
43, 44)

The traumatic consequences of a child's seduction or rape by
an adult are often the result not of the sexual experience itself,
investigators have found, but of the hysterical reaction of parents
to the event. At such a time the child needs parents who are calm
and reassuring. Since parents rarely are, adult-child sexual encounters almost invariably have a negative conditioning effect
on the child. (45)

Positive sexual conditioning occurs when a child has friends
of both sexes and lives in an environment in which nudity is accepted as a matter of course. The very best positive conditioning
comes from the parents' accepting attitude toward sex. If they
enjoy each other physically and show it by touching, kissing,
and caressing in front of their children they are giving their
youngsters the finest sex education possible in our culture. (46,
47, 48)

Fortunately for the continuation of the human race, the sex
drive in most of us is stronger than the cultural training that
would minimize or extinguish it. So is the drive toward intimacy.
Children know that they need love and cuddling even when they
are deprived of it in the home. Attractive children usually manage to get affection elsewhere, if their homes are deficient in that
commodity.

If you remember your childhood as happy, even though your
home was less than warm and accepting, then undoubtedly your
needs for affection were met in other ways and places. If they
weren't met, and if you remember your childhood as unhappy,

this may have acted as a spur to your active search for intimacy and love in adolescence and adulthood. (49, 50)

2: Adolescence

Puberty is a critical time in human sexual development. A sharp upsurge in the production of male and female hormones brings with it both physical and psychological changes, and both bring the burgeoning adolescent into sharp conflict with society. From puberty to the early twenties the male is at the height of his sexuality, with no socially approved outlet. Marriage is economically unfeasible for most, and both premarital sex and masturbation are officially discouraged.

Society winks when the young male manages to evade the sexual prohibitions, but he often does so at great cost to his future sexuality. Many cases of bizarre sexual behavior can be traced to the abnormal sexual environment forced on adolescent males by a society that refuses to recognize their sexual needs.

Females are also handicapped. Though puberty prepares them for sex, just as it does the male, the cultural restrictions are so repressive that they not only inhibit sexual activity but also sexual desire. While boys increase sexual play after the age of nine, in girls sexual play reaches a peak at this age and then goes rapidly downhill, according to the research of Dr. Carlfred B. Broderick, professor of family relations at Pennsylvania State University.

Sexual activity peaks again in women in the late twenties or early thirties, generally after several years of marriage. It takes this long for cultural restrictions and taboos to wear off.

For society is harsh on the woman who transcends sexual prohibitions. Methods of birth control and abortions, even knowledge about them, are frequently denied the unmarried, underage woman, while out-of-wedlock pregnancy is a disgrace she may never live down. The same act of intercourse that proves the boy a man may be used as evidence that the girl is a slut, to be condemned and ostracized.

No wonder some women prefer to turn off their sexuality at puberty rather than face its consequences. What this does to them physically and emotionally during the period of abstinence, researchers have not yet investigated. The aftermath is all too well known. Women's sexual awakening is delayed, with consequent marital difficulties. And large numbers of women never do become orgasmic.

PERSONAL RELATIONS

Because the period of adolescence is physically a time of sexual development, everything that happens to the adolescent is tinged with sexuality. And everything that happens to him affects his sexual development. This includes family stability, even geographic stability. The youngster on the verge of adulthood is weaning himself from his family in order to become a sexually mature person. He is better able to do this in familiar surroundings. If the scene keeps changing he's at a disadvantage. (51)

But families let go reluctantly. Strict parents put up all sorts of obstacles in an attempt to keep their child a child, safely at home. In revolt, teenagers may sneak out on dates their parents don't allow and suffer guilt and remorse as a by-product. (Besides learning to be sneaky.) (52, 53)

Unrecognized jealousy plays a part in the adolescent's difficulties with his family. Very often the parent of the opposite sex becomes possessive and hostile toward the teenager's dates. The child takes this disapproval of his romantic choices as disapproval of himself. (54)

Or the boy at puberty may suddenly shun the sister to whom he has formerly been close, fearing his newly insistent sexuality will shape their relationship in frightening ways. Or she may avoid him for the same reasons. For both, sexuality and intimacy are damped. And the rejected one, not knowing why he was cast off, may develop hampering feelings of inadequacy. (55)

Such feelings are the lot of the adolescent, no longer a child and not yet an adult. Moving from one world to the other, he's unsure of himself. He feels freakish if he has matured either earlier or later than his peers. He worries that his developing sexual characteristics may be inadequate, or that he hasn't properly learned his sex role. (56, 57, 58)

Such worries can be compounded, and self-esteem destroyed, if for any reason, or none at all, the significant adults in his life show that they are worried that he may have homosexual tendencies. His self-esteem can also be shattered by physical differences or defects, or if he is unpopular with his peers. Unfortunately, the conviction of inferiority acquired in adolescence isn't always discarded with maturity. It may be as disfiguring in adulthood as acne scars. (59, 60, 61)

PERSONALITY

Though adolescence is most dramatically the time of sexual maturing, it is also the time that the teenager must prepare himself, in every way, for adulthood. He can do so only if he isn't overwhelmed by his new sexuality. One gauge of this is his ability to maintain meaningful platonic friendships with members of both sexes and to make and carry out, or work toward, both short-term and long-term goals. (62, 63, 64, 65)

Preparing to step out into the world, from the shelter of home and school, means learning about that world and even taking a share of responsibility for it. The person so unadventurous that he doesn't explore beyond the beliefs in which he was brought up is not likely to be interested enough in the inner workings of another's mind to try to know it intimately. And the person so blind he doesn't see the social problems all around him is going to have difficulty looking into the heart of another. (66, 67)

Rigidity militates against intimacy. One needs flexibility to flow into and with the contours of another. Strangely, a fairly reliable index to rigidity is the use of the social drugs favored by contemporaries. The person who, disapproving of the drugs, denies himself the sociability of those who use them is obviously putting other considerations above human relations. However high-principled this may seem to some, it is the person who can share the social drug when this is appropriate, and leave it alone at other times, who is apt to have the capacity to share with others more important things as well. (68)

In contrast, the person who *depends* on drugs to deal with life, or protect himself from it, is usually afraid of his own emotions and can be expected to be afraid of the emotions of others as well. He can communicate only when his inhibitions have been dissolved in chemicals. If this becomes a way of life he retards his development in intimacy as surely as he retards it in every other direction. (69)

Not all adolescent dropouts are voluntary. Frequent or prolonged illness means dropping out too, whether or not it is subconsciously welcomed for that very reason. The isolation of illness in childhood and adolescence has produced geniuses. Sometimes it produces sexual deviates. Almost invariably it retards social and social-sexual development. (70)

SEXUALITY

The healthy teenager welcomes evidence of his sexual maturation with exuberance and curiosity. He delights in his body, uses it joyfully, and acquaints himself with its changing appearance and capacities. (71, 72, 73)

Through masturbation he (and hopefully, she too) prepares himself for his future sexual role, learning the ways in which his body can give him pleasure. This is an important part of sexual education. So important, in fact, that Dr. Alfred C. Kinsey and his associates established that those who had masturbated frequently in adolescence were those with the happiest marital relations in adulthood. More recently, Masters and Johnson have found that a first step in the successful treatment of sexual inadequacies in adults is practice in masturbation, followed by mutual masturbation between partners. (74)

Because youngsters in puberty rarely have heterosexual partners their mutual masturbation usually occurs with members of the same sex. Though this certainly is not an ideal arrangement, the comparison of bodies and genitalia, and learning to give and receive pleasure with a partner, are also part of the educational process.

The most important part of sexual gender identification is learned in the first four or five years of life, according to Dr. John H. Hampson, a psychiatrist at the University of Washington School of Medicine, in Seattle. Despite mutual masturbation, the heterosexual boy's dreams and fantasies will be of girls. And the girl's will be of boys. And both will follow their fantasies to fulfillment when the opportunity affords. (75, 76)

So mutual masturbation won't cause homosexuality in normal youngsters, and masturbation won't cause insanity, impotence, or the growth of hair on the palms of the hands. The danger in both is that the adolescent himself will worry about adverse effects or feel guilty about his sexual activity. Parents, preachers, and teachers often encourage feelings of guilt, insisting that the youngster "sublimate" his sexual desires through activity of other sorts. That's like asking a "hungry youngster to read the classics instead of eating," suggests Dr. Albert Ellis. But the conscientious boy or girl worries that the inability to sublimate sexuality is proof of a flaw in his moral character. (77)

The result can be a strange denial of the body's ability to give pleasure. The pleasure is attributed to the hand (some boys call it "Mary"), from which the self is dissociated. Then the body becomes the "innocent" recipient of the ministrations of the hand.

This conditioning is poor preparation for satisfactory sexual relations with a partner. For the "innocent" body continues to expect to receive pleasure without active involvement and without giving pleasure in return. This disappoints both partners and often sends the owner of the "innocent" body off on an endless fool's quest for the perfect pleasure-giving lover. (78)

In anticipation of their adult sexual roles, healthy, uninhibited postpubertal boys and girls learn their lessons wherever they can. In an effort to find out what sex is all about, and how it's done, they consult dictionaries and encyclopedias, read sexually explicit novels, scientific treatises, and pornography indiscriminately, play the voyeur at bedroom windows and at movies, both legitimate and underground, and discuss the subject endlessly among themselves. In this endeavor to prepare themselves sexually they get little help from adults and gather as much misinformation as knowledge. Despite this, they advance farther along the road to intimacy as a result of their sexual probing than those youngsters who attempt to turn off their sexuality, expecting love to turn it on at some future date and divulge all its secrets in one magic moment. (79, 80)

Of course, it's as impossible to turn off sexuality completely as it is to turn off thirst. The body needs water and it needs sexual expression. So youngsters on guard against their sexual natures inevitably make compromises, always at the sacrifice of intimacy.

Many make it a practice to fall in love with unavailable love objects and then to enjoy (or suffer with) erotic notions and emotions without any danger of physical contact. Others keep the physical expression of love at a minimum by giving other considerations priority, even during romantic interludes. (81, 82)

Girls, in particular, become adept at turning off erotic sensations at a cutoff point they have arbitrarily decided good girls don't go beyond. This may involve localizing all sensations in the lips during a kiss, confining contact to necking, or avoiding petting to climax. The trouble is, of course, that such training doesn't reverse itself as a result of a wedding ceremony. (83, 84, 85, 86)

Not only society but the boys they date make the girls the cops at the sexual corner. The males do this by projecting their own guilt on their partners. "I'm not wicked for wishing to go all the way," they rationalize. "She's a bad girl if she lets me." And she accepts this moral indictment, and tries to maintain the technical virginity still prized in a bride.

Again, the attitude of neither partner is altered by wedding bells. The virgin bride continues to believe that good girls shouldn't have sensual feelings, and her groom continues to believe that through intercourse he is demeaning her. He thus becomes an excellent candidate for the selective impotence that chooses "nice" women and the marriage bed for orgasmic failure. (87, 88)

Many of the sexual inadequacies that trouble adult relationships are the result of adolescent attempts to fit sexual needs to society's strictures. The most common of these is the male who, fearing detection, actually trains himself to become a premature ejaculator by rushing to orgasm in his hidden and forbidden sexual encounters. His speed, and her own fears of detection and/or pregnancy, may also freeze his partner into long-lasting frigidity. (89)

This "take while the taking is good" attitude is not one to foster intimacy. Rather, it is responsible for a good deal of sexual exploitation among adolescents. Males importune females to give them satisfaction and then discard them for more obliging females. Girls, in turn, take advantage of the desperation of the males and then leave them for boys who offer more for their favors. When people become mere sexual objects consequences are not considered. Promiscuity spreads venereal disease. Contraception is neglected, pregnancy degraded, and force accepted. (90, 91, 92, 93, 94, 95)

Unfortunately, many romantics also victimize each other. Their Hollywood-inspired dream that love will conquer all keeps them from doing more than dreaming in preparation for their lovemaking. Lack of knowledge can turn their dream into a nightmare the first time they try to express their love physically. And the idea that contraception would spoil the spontaneity and beauty of the act is a common cause of unwanted pregnancies. (96)

The best preparation an adolescent can have for a satisfying and enduring love life is to fall in love many times and to have his love reciprocated. Through these love experiences he—and she too—will gain the confidence to select a love partner, rather than waiting to be chosen, and will learn the art of wooing. Each will learn also that love is expressed through companionship and the sharing of life's experiences as well as through sexual sharing. (97, 98, 99, 100)

The adolescent who has been fortunate enough to learn these lessons instead of some of the others we have discussed won't be rushed into sexual misadventures. He will learn the pleasure of intimacy at the same time he discovers the pleasures of sex and will practice them both. For such a lucky young adult sexual awakening will be a delightful promise of a joyful future.

Fortunately, we don't stop learning and changing just because we stop growing physically. Not only what we learn in childhood and adolescence but also what we learn later as adults becomes part of our nature and is reflected in our temperament and attitudes, which are measured in the next two sections of the questionnaire.

17

Being — Questions

Section 3: Temperament

This questionnaire has been set up so that up to three people can use it simultaneously. Each places a +, −, or 0 in the column he uses.

ANSWERS
+ + +
− − −
0 0 0

101. Do you have frequent colds? — — —

102. Are you overweight? — — —

103. Do you often have indigestion? — — —

104. Are you often constipated? — — —

105. Do you worry a great deal about your health? — — —

106. Do you often get the blues? — — —

107. Do you dislike active sports? — — —

108. Do you have a quick temper? — — —

ANSWERS

+   +   +
−   −   −
o   o   o

109. Are you irritable when things don't go your way?   — — —

110. Do noisy, happy children annoy you?   — — —

111. Were you happier in the past than you are right now?   — — —

112. Do you feel that your fate is controlled by the stars, the lines on your palms, or the will of a god or gods?   — — —

113. Are you apprehensive about the future?   — — —

114. Do you let unexpressed anger smolder inside you until it explodes?   — — —

115. Are you easily made jealous?   — — —

116. If your intimate partner was unfaithful would you refuse to forgive and forget?   — — —

117. Do you have difficulty making decisions?   — — —

118. Do you feel your intuition is always wrong?   — — —

119. Are you inclined to worry?   — — —

120. Do you feel humiliated when you have to admit that you were wrong?   — — —

121. Would you give up a goal if you had to take chances to reach it?   — — —

ANSWERS

+ + +

— — —

o o o

122. When you go on a vacation do you take your work along? — — —

123. Are you upset when the laugh is on you? — — —

124. Do you usually wear clothes that are dark or neutral in color? — — —

125. When you walk through a restaurant or other public place do you feel that everybody's eyes are on you? — — —

126. Do you do your own thing no matter what the neighbors might think? — — —

127. Can you resist persuasive salesmen? — — —

128. Does a beautiful speaking voice turn you on? — — —

129. Are you always aware of your surroundings? — — —

130. When you hear birds singing do you stop what you're doing to listen with full concentration? — — —

131. Do you like the smell of a clean baby? — — —

132. Do many different kinds of odors delight you? — — —

133. Do you enjoy trying new and different foods? — — —

134. Do you like to be touched?   — — —

135. Are you easily amused?   — — —

136. Do you often do things on the spur of the moment?   — — —

137. Can you sit still through a long committee meeting, lecture, or concert without twiddling your thumbs, wagging your feet, or biting your nails?   — — —

138. Can you usually fall asleep and stay asleep without the use of sleeping pills?   — — —

139. Are you a moderate drinker—rather than a heavy drinker or a teetotaler?   — — —

140. Do you smoke not at all or very little?   — — —

141. Can you put yourself in another's place and experience his joys and sorrows with him?   — — —

142. Are you seriously concerned about social problems even when they don't personally affect you?   — — —

143. Do you think most people can be trusted?   — — —

144. Can you talk to a celebrity or a stranger as easily as you talk to your neighbor?   — — —

145. Do you get along well with sales clerks, waiters, service station attendants, cab and bus drivers?   — — —

ANSWERS
+ + +
— — —
o o o

146. Can you discuss sex in mixed company as
easily as you discuss the weather?
— — —

147. Can you express appreciation for a gift or a
favor without embarrassment?
— — —

148. Do you cry at sad movies?
— — —

149. When you feel affection can you express it
effectively with body and words?
— — —

150. Do you sometimes feel that you have extrasensory perception?
— — —

To calculate your Temperament Intimacy Potential Quotient,
count the minuses with which you have answered questions 101
through 125. Count the pluses you have marked in the answer
slots 126 through 150. Add the two totals. Multiply by two. Subtract the number of zero answers you gave in this section. Record
this final figure in the space provided below, and then proceed to
the fourth section of the questionnaire.

TEMPERAMENT INTIMACY
POTENTIAL QUOTIENT   ____
                             ____
                             ____

Section 4: Attitudes

This questionnaire has been set up so that up to three people can use
it simultaneously. Each places a +, −, or o in the column he uses.

ANSWERS
+ + +
− − −
o o o

151. Do you like yourself?   — — —

152. Do you like others of your own sex?   — — —

153. Do you enjoy spending an evening alone?   — — —

154. Do you vary your schedule so that you don't
perform the same task the first thing every
Monday morning?   — — —

155. Are holidays, birthdays, and anniversaries
important to you?   — — —

156. Is love more important to you than money?   — — —

157. Do you like to give and receive impractical
gifts?   — — —

158. Would you rather be noted for your kindness than for your honesty?   — — —

159. Do you think it is possible to be too rational?   — — —

ANSWERS

	+	+	+
	−	−	−
	o	o	o

160. Have you attended or would you like to attend a sensitivity or encounter group?   — — —

161. Do you believe that physical ills have nothing to do with emotions?   — — —

162. Do you discourage friends from dropping in unannounced?   — — —

163. Do you consider your genitalia less clean than the rest of your body?   — — —

164. Would you feel it a sign of weakness to seek help for a sexual problem?   — — —

165. Are you upset when a homosexual is attracted to you?   — — —

166. Do you think homosexuals are incapable of loving each other?   — — —

167. Are males by nature aggressive and females, by nature, submissive and dependent?   — — —

168. Do you have difficulty carrying on a conversation with someone of the opposite sex?   — — —

169. Do you believe the proper place for a woman is in the kitchen?   — — —

170. Would you mind working for a woman boss?   — — —

ANSWERS

+   +   +

–   –   –

o   o   o

171. Do you feel that menstruation and the menopause disqualify women for important decision-making positions?

— — —

172. Do you believe that men who write poetry are less masculine than athletes?

— — —

173. Are female athletes less feminine than other women?

— — —

174. Do men prefer dumb women to bright ones?

— — —

175. Do most women prefer men with well-developed muscles to men with well-developed emotions?

— — —

176. Do you believe that laws should regulate sexual acts between consenting adults?

— — —

177. Do you feel that only married couples should have sexual intercourse?

— — —

178. In your opinion should unmarried adolescents be denied contraceptives?

— — —

179. Do you think that couples who indulge in oral or anal sex should be liable to prosecution as perverts?

— — —

180. Do you consider women who want abortions immoral or unnatural?

— — —

181. Should husbands be excluded from the delivery room when their wives are having babies?

— — —

182. Do you think that the kibbutz and communes have nothing to teach us?

— — —

183. Should a couple put up with an unhappy marriage for the sake of the children?

— — —

184. Do you think that all mate swappers are unhappily married?

— — —

185. Should older men and women be content without sexual expression?

— — —

186. Are blacks better endowed sexually than whites?

— — —

187. Do you feel that young people today are sexually irresponsible?

— — —

188. Do you believe that pornography increases sexual crimes?

— — —

189. Do you feel a divorcee or widow should forgo sex until her remarriage?

— — —

190. Is sexual continence beneficial to a person's health, strength, wisdom, or character?

— — —

191. Can women feel sexual desire even when they are not in love?

— — —

ANSWERS

+ + +

— — —

o o o

192. Can a loving wife sometimes be sexually unreceptive?   — — —

193. Are some women sexually more receptive during menstruation than at other times?   — — —

194. Is intercourse during a woman's menstrual period as appropriate as at any other time?   — — —

195. Is orgasm as pleasurable for women as it is for men?   — — —

196. Can a man's attempt to bring his partner to orgasm dilute the pleasure he experiences during the sexual act?   — — —

197. Should a woman concentrate on her sensual pleasure during intercourse rather than faking orgasm to please her partner?   — — —

198. Should fun replace goals in sexual relations?   — — —

199. Is pressure for sexual performance frequently a cause of sexual incapacity?   — — —

200. Is it impossible to will an orgasm?   — — —

For this section of the questionnaire count the pluses with which you have answered questions 151 through 160 and questions 191 through 200. Count the minuses in the answer spaces for questions 161 through 190. Add the two totals and multiply the result by two. Subtract all zero answers in this section. That gives you your

ATTITUDES INTIMACY
POTENTIAL QUOTIENT   ____

                             ____

                             ____

Now read the discussion of the two sections of the questionnaire you have just finished, which follows in Chapter 18.

18

Being — Answers

Hippocrates, the father of medicine, taught that the body was composed of four cardinal humors—blood, phlegm, yellow bile, and black bile. Until modern times physicians believed, with the ancient Greek, that even disease was caused by an excess of one or another of the humors. And philosophers attributed the difference in men's natures, or temperaments, to the same phenomenon.

A preponderance of blood "disposed" a man to be sanguine. An excess of phlegm gave him a phlegmatic disposition. He was choleric, or bilious, if he had too much choler, or yellow bile. Black bile caused him to be melancholic.

We no longer believe in the cardinal humors but we still have a tendency to think that man's temperament is inborn. "I can't help it. That's the way I am," we say. Or, "That's my nature." We display our nature through our attitudes and behavior, and assume that these too are immutable.

"I'm naturally shy," we explain in the same way we describe ourselves as tall or short. "I have a bad temper" sounds as unchangeable as "I have a long neck." Sometimes we don't even mention ourselves. We describe our origins and expect others to understand us because they know that our parents were artists or Irish or self-made. Or that we were born under the sign of Libra or Cancer. Or that we're male, or female, or Jewish, or part Indian.

Our explanation for our temperament and attitudes would be more accurate if we detailed the first five years of our lives. Or if we explained that our parents, or other significant adults, expected us to be hot-tempered, or shy, or clumsy, or bright, or stupid, and that we have dedicated ourselves to fulfilling their expectations.

In psychology this is known as the "self-fulfilling prophecy." We internalize another's opinion of us, make it our own, and try to live up (or down) to it. If Junior is told he is "a chip off the old block," and believes it, he'll try to emulate Dad, sometimes in the wrong ways.

If Dad was a successful but hard-drinking businessman, Junior may pick up the wrong cue and become a hard drinker. He's still a chip off the old block and he can excuse his drinking because it "runs in the family."

But even when we correctly find causes of disposition and attitudes in childhood training we have uncovered only part of the reason we are what we are. For the rest we must look to the future. In the words of Dr. Elton Trueblood: "Man is a creature whose present is constantly being dominated by reference to the nonexistent, but nevertheless potent, future. What is *not* influences what *is*."

So, if we don't like what *is* we can change it into what is *not*, or what we think ought to be, by orienting ourselves to the future instead of the past. That's like making a journey. But in order to start the journey we must know not only where we want to go but also where we are in relationship to the goal. What temperament and attitudes have we carried with us out of the past?

3: Temperament

Though we no longer believe in bodily "humors" we are increasingly aware that the condition of the body affects our humor, or state of mind. No one ever felt sanguine when contending with an excess of phlegm, which commonly occurs with the common cold.

On the other hand, the state of mind also affects the condition of the body. And many physicians today feel that the common cold happens most commonly to people when they are psychologically upset.

The symptoms—the tearing eyes and running nose, the difficulty in breathing, the coughing, gagging, and strangling—resemble a child's attempt to suppress his crying. And that's what a cold is, some psychiatrists say, a suppressed cry. It's suppressed because the person feels he shouldn't cry. He may think he's too old. Or he may not want to admit to consciousness the emotional blow, or conflict, that threatens to bring on the weeping reaction. (101)

Because the mind is part of the body, anything that affects one also affects the other. Signals from one to the other are sent not only via the central nervous system but also, by chemical messengers, through the bloodstream. So the toothache precipitates an emotional problem. Or the emotional trouble can manifest itself as a toothache—or pave the way for more serious illnesses such as heart disease or cancer.

The physical process most closely attuned to the emotions is the alimentary, because the child's first gratifications and frustrations are centered around eating, digesting, and eliminating. The infant's first experience of love, warmth, and security is associated with feeding and satiation.

For some the equation of love and food is carried into adulthood. Because they are afraid of intimate relationships, or of their own sexuality, they try to satisfy emotional needs by overeating. The resulting obesity protects them from more mature methods of obtaining affection.

Others overeat when they feel rejected, unloved, or insecure. The result is the same. Their weight increase makes them feel unlovable, which makes them eat more, which makes them weigh more. And both the weight and their low self-esteem hinder or prevent other solutions to their need for affection. (102)

Digestive problems, from heartburn to hyperacidity to ulcers, are frequently psychosomatic in origin. Studies carried out at the Chicago Institute for Psychoanalysis found that such problems occur in people whose wish to be dependent is in conflict with the adult ego, which insists on independence and self-sufficiency. (103)

Although constipation may be a sign of any number of organic ailments, chronic constipation is usually psychological in origin. Studying patients troubled with this condition, Doctors Franz Alexander and W. C. Menninger found that constipated people also suffered from pessimism and a distrust of others, as well as a feeling of being rejected and not loved. Their reaction to their psychological state is similar to the reaction of a child who views evacuation as a gift to adults and refuses to part with this offering if he does not receive affection in return. (104)

When ailments, large or small, are psychosomatic in origin they substitute for conscious, healthy expressions of the emotions. Even when the cause of illness is organic, its psychological effect is to dull interaction with others and with the environment.

But one doesn't have to be ill to do this. The hypochondriac does it just by worrying about illness. His excessive concern with health is an unhealthy form of self-love that leaves little or no room for the love of others. Very often it represents a defense against outgoing love, which the hypochondriac subconsciously fears. (105)

The interdependence of mental and physical well-being is experienced by everyone during periods of depression. The best cure for the blues is activity—a brisk walk or a game of tennis or handball gives the body, and with it the mind, a quick physical pick-me-up. The blues, on the other hand, produce physical lethargy. This is sometimes so heavy that the depressed person can't force himself to physical exertion and a mild, unrecognized depression, with its accompanying sluggishness, becomes a way of life. (106, 107)

The person with the blues succumbs to the dark side of life and infects others with his melancholy. The irritable person, and the one with the hair-trigger temper, try to manipulate their environments and the people around them by threatening to pollute the emotional atmosphere with storm clouds of their own making if things don't go just their way. Instead of enjoying the world

as it is, they try to dictate the way it should be, even to turning
off the healthy, happy activity of children when the exuberance
of the young doesn't match the mood of the temper tyrant. (108,
109, 110)

INDEPENDENCE

Many of our emotional troubles and physical ailments arise
from the conflict between a wish to remain a dependent, cared-
for child and a need to become an independent, coping adult.
The person who hasn't resolved the conflict sees the present as
a struggle and the past as perfect.

He would go back to that dependent time if he could, and
some people actually manage to do that via drugs, the bottle, or
illness. Women manage it most often because our society allows,
and even encourages, women to remain in a state of dependence,
first on the father and then on the husband. It's not a healthy
state. (111)

The dependent adult, man or woman, is rather like a cripple
who must depend on others for all satisfactions. These are the
people who keep astrologers, palmists, and fortunetellers in business. Just because they have given up any attempt to control
their own fate they are frantically worried about it, fear that it
may fall under an evil influence, and seek constantly to foretell
the future or to placate the powers they believe control their
destiny. (112, 113)

For the dependent person things always go wrong, simply because those he has put in charge of his life can't really take
charge. Though the helpless one blames his troubles on the people he clings to, he is afraid to let them know his anger for fear
he will lose their support. So that anger grows within him until
the pressure becomes too great and it explodes. (114)

If, after the explosion, the supporter continues to hold up the
clinging vine, his strength is sapped by parasitic tendrils. The
dependent one is jealous of every interest or activity the other

has, feeling that his own happiness suffers when the other attends to anyone or anything else. (115)

Sometimes this drives the supporting partner to infidelity. Instead of trying to find out what went wrong and righting it, the dependent one blames and reproaches. Betrayal is never forgiven nor forgotten, but used to stoke the fires of resentful anger that the betrayed one calls love. He can't love anybody but himself, of course, and his possessiveness eventually strangles any love that others have for him. (116)

The independent, coping adult takes responsibility for his own life. He considers choices and makes decisions, trusting both his reasoning mind and his intuition. He accepts the fact that he is human and fallible and that, therefore, some of his decisions will be wrong. But he doesn't lose sleep worrying about this possibility. And he doesn't feel he loses face when he makes a mistake. (117, 118, 119, 120)

His life has direction. His goals are important to him and he's not afraid to take risks to reach them. But neither is he so serious that he can't laugh at himself. Nor so future-oriented that he can't enjoy the present. He works hard when he works and forgets his work when it's time to play. (121, 122, 123)

The independent person likes himself, and others, and enjoys contacts with people. He doesn't try to shrink into the background by acting shy or dressing drably. Neither does he imagine that he is so important that all eyes are always on him. He does his own thing and lets the neighbors do theirs. Since he knows what he wants nobody can sell him something he doesn't need. (124, 125, 126, 127)

Is such a person too independent to be an intimate partner? Don't you believe it! It takes a person with self-respect to respect another. It takes someone who can walk alone to keep pace in tandem. It takes courage and strength to love.

"Lose your mind and come to your senses," the Gestalt psychiatrist Fritz Perls used to tell his students. And that's what happens when two people make love. They lose their minds and come to their senses. That is, if they have senses. Some people keep all their senses but sight and hearing in cold storage and use those two only for very practical purposes.

They see one another. They hear the words the other bestows upon them. But they miss the communication because they don't watch what the other is saying, with his facial expression and his body movements. And they don't hear his voice.

Words are used as often to conceal feelings as to communicate them. Bodies and voices are much more honest. You say, "I'm feeling fine," whether or not you are. Someone who has exercised his sight and hearing listens to your voice and watches your body and believes those statements rather than your words.

You expect that, particularly from an intimate partner. For intimate partners wish often to communicate emotions for which there are no words. And how can they do that if one, or both, are blind and deaf?

The chances are you're neither if you respond emotionally to the quality of a speaking voice. If you don't do that it's time to start training your ears, particularly if you're still looking for an intimate partner. Start listening instead. A voice can tell you in a few minutes things you might not learn otherwise.

The person who has trained himself to appear composed can't extend control to his vocal cords. They're exactly as tense as he is inwardly. And so he can't keep an inner anxiety from coming through in his harsh, strained voice. On the other hand, a full, round, pleasant voice can only come from an inner tranquility that leaves the vocal cords relaxed. (128)

Calm, tranquil people are the ones who react to the here and now—an essential for intimacy. They're the ones who drop all other thoughts and concerns to listen to bird songs. They're aware of odors. Not just of perfumes, but of the different smells of different people, houses, seasons, days. They really dig that most human of all smells, the smell of a clean baby. (129, 130, 131)

The sense of smell is the neglected sense in humans. We left it behind when we stopped navigating on all fours, using our noses to warn us of danger or lead us to food and water and sex. Today there is no better indication of the highly sensual person than a well-developed sense of smell. (132)

Closely aligned with the sense of smell is the sense of taste. If the sense of smell is deficient the sense of taste suffers. It suffers also from inhibitions. Some people grow up afraid of new tastes. They equate them with tastes forbidden in infancy. These are the people who find Indian food "smelly" and oral sex "dirty." They are rarely adventurous, either in life or in bed. (133)

Also unadventurous, and certainly not sensual, are people who don't like to be touched. They are the extreme nontouchers. Nontouchers often grow up to be museum curators who put "Do Not Touch" signs above every piece of sculpture or art work that must be touched to be known.

Touchers are the people who disobey the signs. They also touch fabrics, animals, and other people, not only with their fingertips but with their cheeks, and lips, and arms, and bodies. They like to cuddle and snuggle and stroke and be stroked. Touchers make ideal intimate partners. (134)

So do people who are always aware of their surroundings. These are usually people whose senses, all of them, are finely tuned and alert and operating in the present. They don't take themselves, or others, too seriously. They are adventurous and easily amused. If a new experience presents itself on the spur of the moment they will go with it, despite any upset to schedule. (135, 136)

Strangely, just because they have so many ways of relating to the moment, including relaxation, these are the same people who can sit still through long periods that make others nervous. And they have no trouble turning off all their senses and falling asleep.

That's because they are receptive not only to signals from the outside world but also to signals from within. They know what they feel and aren't afraid to feel it. If it's boredom, they don't fight it nervously but relax into it. If it's weariness, they don't fight that either, but welcome restoring sleep. (137, 138)

Such people are never heavy drug users, drinkers, or smokers. They don't need drugs or drink to release their emotions so that they can communicate them to others.

The inability to communicate feelings, recent research indicates, is a common cause of drug abuse and alcoholism. People who depend on chemicals for emotional release have a deep emotional need that they can't satisfy in the sober state.

Smokers, on the other hand, cut off this need at its source.

Reaching for a cigarette is a way of turning off emotion, of calling a halt to feelings before they are even experienced. The smoker reaches for a cigarette instead of a hand. He responds not to an emotion but to a fear of one. And he responds always in the same way, whether the aborted feeling be one of love, grief, hate, or anger. Lighting up is a way of cooling off intimacy. (139, 140)

EMPATHY

Can you put yourself in another's place and experience his joys and sorrows with him? That's empathy. Sounds an easy thing to do, doesn't it? But, in fact, it's difficult. It's difficult because instead of experiencing along with someone we tend to evaluate, judge, and advise. That's not empathy. That's playing mother-in-law. (141)

Playing mother-in-law can destroy an intimate relationship. Nonjudgmental empathy can build one. But empathy isn't like a water faucet that you can turn on and off at will. It's a character trait, like honesty, that grows stronger with use. The person who brings empathy to an intimate relationship takes it with him everywhere. His concern is with human beings, even with those he doesn't know, facing problems he has never faced. (142)

The empathetic person likes people and therefore trusts them. He values them for their uniqueness, not for superficial reasons. He's not awed by the celebrity, or embarrassed by the stranger. Neither does he use people—waiters and service station attendants, for instance—as if they were service mechanisms instead of human beings. Nor does he impose his value judgments on others, censoring what they should hear or say. (143, 144, 145, 146)

The person with empathy cares about people and is able to communicate his caring. He can receive gratefully and graciously, as well as give. He can cry when he feels sad and reach out to others when he feels affection. And he is *there* for others. So much so that they, and he, often feel he has extrasensory perception. (147, 148, 149)

Whether or not the phenomenon is ESP the empathetic person does sense the unexpressed thoughts, feelings, and needs of family, friends, and lovers. Even at a distance he stays tuned to their wavelengths. For, in fact, he is as close to them as he is to his own heart. (150)

4: *Attitudes*

Attitudes are much like eyes. Not only do they tell people a great deal about you, but they determine the way you see yourself, the world, and others. A person with astigmatic vision can see several fuzzy, overlapping moons in the sky. Not because there are several moons there, but because his vision is faulty.

It is possible to have astigmatic attitudes as well as eyes. When this happens your view of the world is askew. Even your view of you is affected.

Indeed, your attitudes toward yourself play a central role in the way you see the world. If you find yourself unlovable you expect others to find you that way too. And for the most part they will take your evaluation of yourself and react to you accordingly. That makes them unloving in your eyes, and so you build more barriers against them, an activity they view as hostile. Seeing their reactions, you likewise find them hostile, and decide the world is a cold, unfriendly place.

An entirely different cycle of interactions is set up if you are able to love yourself. Then others also see you as lovable and offer you affection. And surrounded by love instead of barriers, you find the world a warm, accepting place. (151)

Some people understand this in theory but think it doesn't apply to them. They like themselves, they insist. But if at the same time the man says he doesn't like other men, and the woman declares that she can't abide the company of females, there is reason to suspect that neither really accepts himself either. It's difficult to like the self while rejecting the sex of which the self is a member. (152)

Another test of how well you really like yourself is whether or not you enjoy spending time in your own company. The person who can't spend an evening by himself doesn't really care much for himself. "The ability to be alone is the condition for the ability to love," says Dr. Erich Fromm. It's not love but dependency when someone needs another just to have company. (153)

The self isn't a single, simple unit. It is the product of everything that has happened to it and many of its facets are contradictory. The Transactional Analysts group the different parts of the self into the *child*, the *parent*, and the *adult*. When a person is operating as an effective mature being, the three parts of his personality feed him data which the *adult* processes and acts on. At other times the three parts of his being may struggle for control, or his *adult* may give in to the *parent* or the *child* just to keep the peace.

When the *parent* is in charge the person may appear to be functioning efficiently but there is little joy or spontaneity in his life. He must start the work week by performing the same tasks every Monday morning, even though more important jobs need doing. Though he might not admit that he would choose money (security) over love, his *parent* drives him to do this repeatedly as he ignores life's ritual times for the work routine and gives the boss's demands on his time and attention priority over the needs of loved ones. (154, 155, 156)

The *parent* insists that gifts must be useful rather than symbols of love. "Don't waste hard-earned money on frippery," is the admonition. The *parent* part of the personality sees the self as a stubborn *child* that must be driven to do what is good for it rather than what it wishes to do. The *parent*-ruled person believes in will power and honesty and has an idea that his own wishes and his feelings of empathy are childish and therefore suspect. When the *adult* is in charge of the personality it knows, with Rollo May, that the will can't be effective without the wish. And that kindness often can be truer than honesty. (157, 158)

The *parent* cautions the child to reason and think, often without providing sufficient or reliable data to reason with. The educational system reinforces the commandment. Consequently, most of us place too much reliance on our thought processes and are completely out of touch with our emotions. (159)

The rise in popularity of sensitivity, or encounter, groups in recent years is a sign that we realize this and that we're looking for ways to strengthen the *adult*-oriented *child* within us. At his best the *child* in our natures is spontaneous, feeling, and outgoing. But he can also be uncertain and afraid. (160)

When the *child* is fearful he very often takes refuge from his fears in illness, as he used to in childhood. And then he treats his ailments with pills alone, never applying insight. He uses illness to acquire attention and sympathy, which he equates with love. (161)

The healthy *child* in us is delighted by the unexpected surprise. The frightened *child* becomes more frightened. He sees the unexpected, even the unexpected arrival of friends, as a threat to his safely ordered world, and his panic when faced with the unexpected proves to him once again that he is inadequate. (162)

Sex, the forbidden, also panics the frightened *child*. He may deal with sexual fears by disowning his genitals. They aren't part of "clean little me," but dirty equipment necessary for some unpleasant functions and best forgotten otherwise. (163)

Even when the frightened *child* in our natures knows he has some very basic sex problems, he can neither face them nor seek help. To ask for help would increase his uncomfortable feeling of helplessness. And anyway he has a vague, immature idea that even the desire for satisfactory sex would not be approved by the *parent*. He half suspects that unsatisfactory sex, or none at all, is a quite appropriate punishment for his unquenchable sexuality. (164)

Nowhere is the frightened *child* in us more evident than in our treatment of homosexuals. For few of us have learned to handle the components within us that we associate with the other sex. Women are frightened of their impulses toward aggression, men of their desires for dependence. Both wonder if these secret, hidden feelings mean that they're not "normal." These fears surface when they are approached by someone they have been taught to consider as not normal. Has he found them out? Does he know the worst?

To keep such fears at bay we ostracize those who arouse them. We deny them the right to love and marry. We condemn and punish them. Whenever we do this to others we diminish our capacity to love. (165, 166)

ATTITUDES TOWARD OTHERS

A battle of the sexes goes on within each of us and contaminates our relations with the opposite sex. Just as we project our unacceptable feelings on homosexuals, and then punish them for these qualities, so we give to the other sex the traits we dislike in ourselves. We define masculinity as aggressive and femininity as submissive. Both words are heavily loaded with negative connotations. (167)

With so little respect for the qualities with which we have endowed the opposite sex, we have great difficulty getting together across sexual lines. Men and women can mate, in silence and darkness, but they can't carry on a conversation. They're more comfortable when they're segregated—men running the world, women helping in subservient positions or, preferably, running their homes. A woman boss breaks the pattern and sounds the panic button. (168, 169, 170)

Because strong males can't admit the real reasons for their female phobia they invent "scientific" explanations that turn women's miraculous life-nurturing abilities into crippling disabilities. Then, to keep from feeling crippled themselves, men must shun everything they have labeled feminine, from long hair to child care to poetry. Since much that is called feminine is rewarding and creative, men who renounce everything feminine rob themselves. (171, 172)

Women too diminish themselves as persons when they adopt a narrowly defined feminine role. Blonde may be beautiful, but dumb is dull. Helplessness is a handicap. And a lack of interest in anything but self is boring.

There are signs that artificial sexual distinctions are on the way out, though the signs are more evident than are actual changes. Many of the look-alike young men and women of the Now generation are more willing to adopt each other's clothing and hair styles than to give up the traditional sexual roles of dominant male and dependent female.

Still, surveys show that companionship qualities are the ones marriage-minded young people are looking for in future mates. The men want women who are athletic, adventurous, independent, and intelligent, qualities that weren't considered very feminine a few short years ago. The women want men who are communicative, sensitive, educated, and intelligent. And some of those traits men are only now beginning to cultivate. (173, 174, 175)

SEXUAL ATTITUDES

Sex is the only natural physiological function that is legislated against. It is surrounded by legal taboos and restrictions. These laws deny sexual expression to all but the married, reinforcing this restriction with prohibitions on the distribution of contraceptive information and devices. (176, 177, 178)

Even the married are governed by laws that reach into the privacy of their bedrooms, prescribing penalties for "unnatural" sex acts and denying couples the right to terminate unwanted pregnancies that result from "natural" copulation. Even when they want the baby, society often denies the parents the right to have it together. The husband is seldom allowed to help his wife through labor and even more rarely permitted in the delivery room. And this, although psychologists have found that women have easier deliveries when the husband is present. Also husbands adjust better to their new roles, and the experience strengthens the relationship. (179, 180, 181)

To assure that sex takes place primarily within wedlock, marriage is easy and cheap, divorce difficult, expensive, and socially and sociologically disapproved. Nevertheless, the divorce rate soars. And though this would seem to suggest that the nuclear family in its present form often fails to meet the needs of individuals or society, variations, such as the kibbutz and the commune, are more often deplored as a threat to marriage rather than explored as a genuine way of life that many find more satisfactory. There is evidence, for instance, that children are happier in communes than they are in many nuclear families. There is also evidence that children are unhappier in cold or bickering families, held together "for their sakes," than they are when divorce puts an end to family dissension, even though it separates the parents. (182, 183)

People who experiment with alternatives to monogamous marriage and sexual fidelity not only run afoul of the law but also face bitter social censure. Yet researchers have found that many of the experimenters (most mate swappers, for instance) are committed to their own marriages and are searching for ways to prevent their erosion through sexual monotony or their destruction by the outside emotional entanglements that often result from secret adulterous liaisons. (184)

Marriage in its present form leaves increasingly large numbers of people without approved sexual outlets, thus promoting jealousy and friction between the haves and the have-nots. Some anxious married couples protect their union from predators, real and imagined, by segregating themselves in neighborhoods and suburbs from which singles, adolescents, the elderly, and members of other races and religions are excluded. They excuse these exclusions by building myths about the unbridled and dangerous sexuality of the banned.

The elderly who still have a healthy interest in sex become dirty old men and women, according to the myths. The sexual appetites and endowments of blacks and other "different" groups, including adolescents, are exaggerated so that protection from them can legitimately be demanded. Lonely men without partners who seek sexual stimulation from pornography or buy a night of simulated love from a prostitute become potential monsters who must be protected from their sexual impulses by the outlawing of their only sources of sexual release. To be socially accepted, single women must remain "pure." (185, 186, 187, 188, 189, 190)

Purity has long been considered a natural state for woman, who is presumed to experience no sexual desires that aren't inspired by love. Even when loved and loving she is supposed to be able to turn off desire until her love receives the marriage stamp of society's approval. After which she is assumed to be in perpetual rut, ready whenever her mate is. (191, 192)

If her own peak of biological arousal comes at the time of menstruation, as it does for many women, she is told to ignore her desire for esthetic reasons. When she fails to reach orgasm she is asked to forget the uncomfortable physical consequences and suppose that she has reached a pleasure peak by giving pleasure to her mate. The sensuous "J" advises *The Sensuous Woman* to increase her partner's pleasure by playing Sarah Bernhardt in bed and faking orgasm. (193, 194)

Does this really increase his pleasure? Reading Dr. David Reuben's *Everything You Ever Wanted to Know About Sex*, you begin to suspect that the female's faked orgasm only increases the male's anxiety. For Dr. Reuben goes to a good bit of trouble to tell the male exactly how to detect a fake orgasm.

If the female is willing to give him this gift of pleasure, why should he question it? Possibly because pleasure isn't his goal. For today's sexual athlete, performance is all. The man's performance demands that *he* bring *her* to orgasm. If she fakes the climax, he has failed and the show is hers.

Rather a competitive picture of what should be the most intimate of human relationships, isn't it? She pretending a pleasure she doesn't experience. He performing valiantly, and then playing detective to find out whether or not he has truly earned another gold star for manhood.

Is that really what these two had in mind when they pledged that "with my body I thee worship"? Hardly. Somewhere along the line the body was reduced to a penis and a vagina. Worship was translated into performance. And the object of the sexual encounter became the orgasm.

Orgasm that happens as a part of physical communication between intimate partners is a wonderful experience. Equally so for both. But it loses much of its magic and luster, and sometimes becomes an impossible achievement, when it becomes the sole goal of sexual performance. (195, 196, 197)

The pressure for performance robs sex of much of its joy. What should be a relaxing, renewing, loving experience becomes a test for both partners. Eventually the very effort to perform can remove the ability.

The pressure for performance is a factor in almost every case of sexual inadequacy. So important a factor is it, in fact, that Masters and Johnson find the elimination of this pressure a vital first step in treating all sexual incapacity. Often it is also the cure.

Couples who would avoid sexual troubles and keep the pleasure in their lovemaking would do well to concentrate on pleasure rather than performance—the moment-by-moment sensual pleasure that their physical closeness brings. Orgasm can be a high point in that pleasure. But since orgasm can not be forced or willed it makes an elusive goal. Wiser to heed the words of Dallas therapist Dr. Emma Lee Doyle, who advises: "Take down your sexual goal posts and enjoy the whole ball game, for time-outs, water breaks, and even penetrations can be fun." (198, 199, 200)

You express your temperament and attitudes by your behavior, testing these always against the satisfactions they bring. Through your behavior you relate to the rest of the world. And reaction to your behavior largely determines how others, both strangers and intimates, relate to you. The last sections of the questionnaire, which follow, test your social and sexual behavior patterns.

19

Behaving—Questions

Section 5: Social Behavior

This questionnaire has been set up so that up to three people can use it simultaneously. Each places a +, −, or o in the column he uses.

ANSWERS
+ + +
− − −
o o o

201. Do you exercise occasionally instead of daily?

— — —

202. Would a nutritionist be appalled by your diet?

— — —

203. Do you often skip a daily bath?

— — —

204. After you bathe does someone else clean the bathtub?

— — —

205. Are you indifferent to your home surroundings?

— — —

206. Do you consider it a waste of money to buy flowers for yourself and others?

— — —

207. Do you wear any old thing around the house?

　　— — —

208. When you see an art object you would like for your home do you pass it by if buying it would mean going without lunches for a while?

　　— — —

209. Do you think it pretentious to dine by candlelight when alone or with members of your immediate family?

　　— — —

210. Are you often bored?

　　— — —

211. Do Sundays depress you?

　　— — —

212. Do you frequently get the jitters?

　　— — —

213. Do you dislike the work you do to earn a living?

　　— — —

214. Would you rather be underpaid than ask for a raise?

　　— — —

215. Do you think the carefree life of a hippie would have no delights for you?

　　— — —

216. Do you watch TV selectively rather than constantly?

　　— — —

217. Do you read general periodicals rather than magazines designed especially for your gender?

　　— — —

ANSWERS

+ + +
— — —
o o o

218. Have you read any good books lately? — — —

219. Do you often daydream? — — —

220. Do you sometimes enjoy going barefoot? — — —

221. Does music often move you to dance spontaneously? — — —

222. Do you like to hold and fondle pets? — — —

223. Do you like many different kinds of art, including modern, nonrepresentational paintings? — — —

224. Do you enjoy looking at an attractive person of the opposite sex? — — —

225. Was last Saturday night's activity different from that of the previous Saturday night? — — —

226. Do you find it easy to talk to new acquaintances? — — —

227. Are you always making new friends? — — —

228. Do you communicate with others through touch as well as through words? — — —

229. Do you communicate effectively enough so that you rarely hurt others unintentionally? — — —

230. Do you practice your charms on members of your family? — — —

ANSWERS
+   +   +
—   —   —
o   o   o

231. Do you avoid joining clubs or organizations?   __ __ __

232. Do you pride yourself on never flirting with
strangers?   __ __ __

233. Do you worry more about how you look to
a prospective love partner than about how
you make him feel?   __ __ __

234. Are you afraid that if people knew the real
you they wouldn't like you?   __ __ __

235. Does fear of rejection keep you from approaching people you would like to know
better?   __ __ __

236. Do you usually fall in love at first sight?   __ __ __

237. Do you always fall in love with someone
who resembles your parent of the opposite
sex?   __ __ __

238. Do you tend to fall in love with persons of
whom your parents strongly disapprove?   __ __ __

239. Do you think love is all you need to make
you happy?   __ __ __

240. Do you take a need for a degree of independence on the part of your intimate part-
ner as a rejection of the relationship?   __ __ __

241. Can you accept your loved one's anger and
still believe in his love?   __ __ __

ANSWERS
+ + +
— — —
o o o

242. Do you express your thoughts and feelings to your loved one?

    — — —

243. Do you talk over disagreements with your intimate partner rather than brooding about them?

    — — —

244. Do you keep old loves out of a love relationship?

    — — —

245. Can you accept without jealousy the fact that your intimate partner has loved others before you?

    — — —

246. Would you refuse to punish an intimate partner by withholding sex?

    — — —

247. Do you use sex to hasten healing after a quarrel with your loved one?

    — — —

248. Can you accept a partner's disinterest in sex without feeling rejected?

    — — —

249. Do you prepare for intercourse with effective contraception and then refuse to let worry spoil your lovemaking?

    — — —

250. Can you accept occasional sessions of unsatisfactory sex without blaming yourself or your partner?

    — — —

This time around count the minus answers for questions 201 through 215 and questions 231 through 240. Count the pluses for questions 216 through 230 and for questions 241 through 250. Add the two totals, multiply by two, and then subtract all zero answers. Record the result in the space below.

SOCIAL BEHAVIOR INTIMACY
POTENTIAL QUOTIENT   _____

Now answer the questions in the last section of the questionnaire.

Section 6: Sexual Behavior

This questionnaire has been set up so that up to three people can use it simultaneously. Each places a +, −, or o in the column he uses.

ANSWERS
+ + +
− − −
o o o

251. Do you consider yourself as sexy as other people?   ___ ___ ___

252. Are you proud of your sexual equipment?   ___ ___ ___

253. Do you keep your genitals as clean as your face and hands?   ___ ___ ___

254. Do you consider the genitals as respectable as other parts of your body?   ___ ___ ___

255. Do you enjoy bathing with your intimate partner?   ___ ___ ___

256. Are you aware of, and do you like, the smell of your partner's body?

— — —

257. Do you like the taste of your loved one's genitals?

— — —

258. When without other sexual outlets do you masturbate regularly?

— — —

259. Do you know the most sexually sensitive parts of the genitals of both sexes?

— — —

260. Is the clitoris the only organ in the human body whose sole function is sexual pleasure?

— — —

261. Is the female's smaller clitoris less sexually sensitive than the male's penis?

— — —

262. Do you refuse to let memories, or anticipation, of exciting sessions of lovemaking interfere with your daily duties?

— — —

263. Do you refuse your partner's sexual overtures on weekday mornings because enjoying them might make one of you late for work?

— — —

264. Do you dislike making love outdoors?

— — —

265. Is it a matter of indifference to you whether or not your partner has an orgasm?

— — —

266. Is mutual orgasm necessary for satisfying sex?

— — —

267. Should a man think of other things during coitus in order to give the woman time to come to orgasm?

— — —

268. Should a man coat his penis with an anesthetizing ointment to prolong his sexual performance?

— — —

269. During intercourse does the clitoris always receive all the stimulation it can handle?

— — —

270. Does the male know best what will please his female partner?

— — —

271. If the intimate couple relaxes and just gives and enjoys sensual pleasure during intercourse are they likely to miss out on orgasm for both?

— — —

272. Is a multi-orgasmic woman a nymphomaniac?

— — —

273. Do you think intercourse provides your genital muscles with all the exercise they need?

— — —

274. Is the male's erection under his voluntary control?

— — —

275. If sexual stimulation is continued, can the male be aroused again immediately after ejaculation?

— — —

ANSWERS

	+	+	+
	—	—	—
	o	o	o

276. Will oral stimulation sometimes help men attain firmer erections?

— — —

277. Can orgasms achieved orally be as satisfying as coital orgasms?

— — —

278. Is it a myth that females ejaculate during orgasm?

— — —

279. Is the male ejaculate harmless if swallowed?

— — —

280. Despite legal bans, is oral sex popular in our society today?

— — —

281. If your partner wanted to try anal sex, would you?

— — —

282. Should couples be guided by the pleasure principle in their sexual practices?

— — —

283. Is the male-superior position inferior for a woman's active participation in the sexual act?

— — —

284. Does the lateral, side-by-side position for coitus permit the greatest freedom of movement for both partners?

— — —

285. Does it excite you when your partner proposes a new time or place for lovemaking?

— — —

286. Do you find that a variety of positions adds zest to your lovemaking?

— — —

ANSWERS

+ + +
— — —
o   o   o

287. Can a small man have a large penis? — — —

288. Does a small penis usually expand more on erection than a large one? — — —

289. Can a small penis provide as much pleasure during intercourse to both partners as a large one? — — —

290. Is an uncircumcised penis as sensitive to sexual stimulation as a circumcised organ? — — —

291. Does a vasectomy affect a man's potency? — — —

292. Is coitus interruptus (withdrawal before ejaculation) an effective method of birth control? — — —

293. Is masturbation the cause of premature ejaculation? — — —

294. Is premature ejaculation impossible to correct? — — —

295. Should a man engage in sex sparingly during his middle years in order to stretch his potency into his later years? — — —

296. Is the loss of sexual desire and capacity a natural part of aging? — — —

297. Should a man who exercises too little and eats and drinks too much expect to have as long a sex life as a more health-conscious male? — — —

ANSWERS

+ + +

— — —

0 0 0

298. Is it unusual for a woman's sexual desire to increase after menopause?

— — —

299. Can the capacity for sexual pleasure be used up by sexual activity?

— — —

300. Is sexual intercourse for you always a serious ritual rather than an uninhibited romp?

— — —

To calculate your score for this final section of the questionnaire count the plus answers for questions 251 through 260 and for questions 276 through 290. Count the minus answers for questions 261 through 275 and for questions 291 through 300. Add the two totals. Multiply by two. Then subtract all zero answers for the section. The result is your

SEXUAL INTIMACY
POTENTIAL QUOTIENT   ——
                      ——
                      ——

Now that you have the scores from all six sections of the questionnaire, you are in a position to calculate your final IPQ score. Before you do that, however, you will want to read the discussion of the Behavior sections of the questionnaire, which follows in the next chapter. We have therefore given directions for calculating your final IPQ at the end of Chapter 20.

20

Behaving — Answers

Your day by day behavior is influenced by your childhood training, your temperament, and your attitudes. It is the *you* that other people know.

Your behavior also shapes and molds and changes you, a fact that the behavioral psychologists use successfully in the treatment of neurosis, psychosis, and drug addiction. They have found that when people "act as if" they were sane, or not dependent on drugs, they become more rational, or less desirous of their chemical crutches. Depressed people actually become happier when they "act as if" they were happy. And frightened people lose some of their fear when they put on a brave front.

This process works continuously in daily life. And though adults rarely realize that it operates for them, they use it regularly with children, rewarding desired behavior to reinforce it and withholding rewards for undesirable behavior. When the process fails, it does so because the child doesn't understand what part of his behavior prompted the reward or because the adults don't know what part of their behavior has reinforced the child's.

The nursery school tot who pleases his parents by bringing home a finger painting of a mermaid may not understand that the approval he has won is for his artistic effort. He may decide that his parents are mad for mermaids and therefore confine his artistry to this particular subject.

Another child, anxious for attention, may get it not for a painting but for misbehavior. The parents feel that by punishing they discourage the mischief, but the child repeats it because he prefers punishing attention to no attention at all.

The same kind of reinforcement often produces nagging wives. If they can't get love and approval with constructive behavior they settle for the angry response elicited by nagging. They prefer it to being ignored.

We also reinforce our own behavior patterns. "I deserve a night on the town," we say, sometimes because we feel we've worked hard to earn it, sometimes because everything has gone wrong. It's easy enough, with irresponsible actions, to make everything go wrong another day in order to earn another reward. In this way habits are built, some bad and some good.

5: Social Behavior

Habits are built on day by day behavior. And it is through daily actions that we reveal ourselves most clearly. The person who has a regular program of exercise, diet, and cleanliness respects his body and, by extension, himself. If he habitually lets someone else clean the bathtub after him, pick up his towels, and wash the dishes when he is through with his meal, there is reason to suspect that his respect for humanity stops at the boundaries of his own skin. The person who uses a love relationship to make a personal servant of the one he loves has confused love with exploitation. (201, 202, 203, 204)

The one who really understands love takes responsibility for keeping himself and his home neat and attractive, whether or not he lives with a loved one. Even alone, he builds the behavior habits that can be depended on to keep alive a future intimate relationship. If he buys flowers for his own pleasure he probably won't stint on the little things that give pleasure to another. (205, 206)

He knows that he can be comfortable without being slovenly.

And he's willing to spend time, attention, and money on leisure clothes and the art objects that surround him daily. If he likes to dine by candlelight when being entertained he doesn't deny himself that pleasure just because he isn't entertaining others in his home. (207, 208, 209)

Such a person is rarely bored, even when alone for long periods, because he has developed the habit of pleasing himself. He's not dependent on others to amuse him or to structure his time. He looks forward to Sundays, not as dull days when he has difficulty finding something to do, but rather as weekly gifts of time to spend for his own satisfaction. (210)

Not everyone who dreads Sundays and other holidays admits this dread, or consciously recognizes it. In our work-worshipping society many people suffer from what the psychologists have labeled "Sunday neurosis," or an inability to enjoy a nonworking day. They've a compulsion to work, and suffer severe attacks of the jitters when idle. (The *parent* within them despises sloth.) (211, 212)

They satisfy the compulsion to labor by taking work home with them over the weekend. That way they save themselves the Sunday blues while insisting they would love nothing more than a genuine holiday. And they cash in on a little sympathy on the side.

Of course, there are people who sometimes *have* to work on Sundays. They are people who love their work enough to sacrifice free time to it when necessary. Then when the pressure is off they can relax and enjoy their leisure.

Most Sunday neurotics don't enjoy their work, any more than they enjoy free time. For them work is unpleasant by definition. Something to be endured, not relished. It would never occur to them to look for work they might find agreeable, since this would put an end to the suffering by which they lay claim to a certain nobility of spirit. For the same reason they don't ask for raises even when they feel they deserve them. Although they themselves hate working, they hate people who manage to live without working even more. They want everybody to suffer.

Obviously, they make rather poor intimate partners for anyone who is not also masochistic. (213, 214, 215)

BEHAVIOR AT PLAY

Television might be counted one of our more effective methods of birth control. It operates by keeping intimate partners apart. After an evening of lolling in front of the flickering set people are in a state akin to that of hypnosis. And they have been hypnotized not into making love but into remaining television spectators through the Tonight Show, the Late Show, and the Late Late Show, until they can no longer hold their eyes open. Television addicts are more often passive than passionate. (216)

People who read in the evening may appear just as passive but their imaginations are working at their direction and at the pace they set. However, a woman curled up with one of the women's magazines and a man stretched out with his favorite he-man periodical may be within touching distance of each other, but they are still worlds apart.

Segregation according to sex, which is disappearing from the rest of our lives, lingers still among slick magazines. *She* reads how to successfully bake a cake, rear a child, save on steak, and keep her man fascinated. *He* reads how to be a success in business, on the stock market, at the races, and with the women. He learns that a woman is a sex object. She learns that a man is a meal ticket. What neither of them ever learn is how a sex object and a meal ticket can communicate. (217)

There are still some authors and publishers of book-length sentimental novels for women and treat-'em-rough fiction for males. But, on the whole, readers of books become communicators. And they practice communication, because the book won't be picked up and finished unless there is enough interest to keep the reader thinking about it between reading sessions. People who are thinking are people who have something to talk about. (218)

Creative people are usually communicators too, because they're bursting with ideas that need a sounding board. Many of these ideas arise in daydreams. Everybody daydreams a little every day, but creative adults do more dreaming while awake than others. Researchers have found that such people use their daydreams not only to generate new ideas but to plan and anticipate the future and to change mood at will. Because daydreamers are receptive to new concepts, and because daydreaming is a method of relaxation, daydreamers listen well—a rare ability and a real plus for intimacy. (219)

People with intimacy potential are people whose senses are alive. They like the feel of grass and sand and carpet under their bare feet. Music sets them dancing and pets set them stroking. And their senses are adventurous. They don't turn away from a painting because it's unusual. They explore it with their eyes as other adventurers explore foreign lands, each wishing to broaden his horizons. (220, 221, 222, 223)

Nor do people with a propensity for intimacy dismiss the familiar by categorizing it, particularly not if it's a human of the opposite sex. But this categorizing occurs even among men who pride themselves on girl watching. They watch legs, or bosoms, according to their specialty. And often they notice nothing else about the girl or girls they claim have attracted them. They are even more short-sighted when it comes to their own wives or intimate partners, a failing that does nothing for the relationship. (224)

Women are more apt to see their intimate partners clearly, but all too often they see them critically as well. They are so busy trying to correct flaws that they haven't time to appreciate the assets that first attracted them. As for strange men, many women pride themselves on looking at them with eyes blind to all but the fact that they are male.

It's an unusual woman, and a sensuous one, who really looks at a man and who, in her imagination, feels his lips kissing her, notes earlobes meant for nipping, fantasies the texture of his hair in her fingertips and the contours of his body fitted against her own. Whether or not they are consciously aware of it, men respond to this sentient appreciation. So do women, for that matter. It's all too rarely that either is regarded at first glance, or even second, as anything but a representative of his or her sex.

BEHAVIOR WITH OTHERS

The person who feels he has no talent for playing the piano usually doesn't try. He can enjoy music by listening to records or attending concerts. The person who feels he has no talent for interpersonal relations is not in such a fortunate position. The quality of his life depends on his ability to interact with others at home, at work, at play.

If he has difficulty interacting he very often gives up the effort, as if he had no more need for this facility than he had a need to play a musical instrument. He spends his evenings in the same way, with the same people, and gains no practice at all in making and keeping friends. (225)

His inexperience shows. He has nothing to say to new acquaintances, and so they rarely become more. Body contact frightens him. When circumstances force communication on him he often finds that he hurts people without meaning to do so. This causes him to retreat even farther into his shell. (226, 227, 228, 229)

That's exactly the wrong reaction. What the socially inept person needs is practice, practice, practice. That's what the socially adept person has been doing all his life. He started learning to please members of the opposite sex by pleasing the opposite-sex members of his family—parents, siblings, cousins, or close neighbors. He polishes his social skills in clubs and organizations. He practices his charm on clerks, people at bus stops, and travelers in subway trains. He collects their smiles, laughter, and flirting as signs of his progress.

Girls who have practiced this find it easy to spark interest in the men who interest them, and to keep that interest growing. The girl who has always waited for a man to speak to her usually finds herself doing more waiting than conversing. And when a man finally does take the initiative she discovers that all her waiting has not prepared her to respond effectively. (230, 231, 232)

We are constantly bombarded with messages telling us that if we wear the right clothes, the right makeup and after-shave lotion, shampoo with the proper liquid, smoke sexy cigarettes, and don't have bad breath, we'll make a hit with those we meet. But that's not the way it's done.

To find out why men respond to one woman instead of another, researchers gave pictures of pretty women to two groups of men. While each man looked over the pictures to select the woman he would most like to date, he heard an erratic thumping in the background. One group of men was told that the thumping had nothing to do with the experiment. Their selection of pictures followed the laws of chance.

Men in the second group were told that the background thumping was an amplification of their own heartbeats. Each of these men invariably chose as his ideal date the woman whose picture he saw when the thumping was fastest.

Though the experiment wasn't repeated with female subjects there is no reason to believe that they wouldn't react in like manner. Whether male or female, you respond not to the way a person looks but to the way he makes you feel. If he makes your heart beat faster you prefer him to others. The heart is more often affected by a glance, a word, or a touch than by an antiperspirant. (233)

How well you give, and respond to, heart-accelerating messages depends on the practice you've had, your self-esteem, and your courage. If you fear that people won't like you if they really know you, then you'll tend to keep them at arm's length. And it's rather difficult to set hearts beating faster at that distance. Similarly, you'll miss many opportunities for close and rewarding relationships if you are so afraid of rejection that you never take the initiative in establishing one. (234, 235)

BEHAVIOR IN LOVE

People who fall in love at first sight aren't really interested in a close relationship with another. They are more interested in making a real live person conform to their fantasy images of an ideal mate. In rare instances this happens. More frequently, the real live person has only a superficial resemblance to the lover's fantasy and refuses to be remade. Love at first sight is usually short-lived. Still, people who can't give up their fantasies continue to fall hard for people who appear to meet them, and their disillusionment matches the fall. (236)

Very often these are people who are looking for a replacement for a childhood love. This love might have been an older brother or sister. More often it was the parent of the opposite sex. If the childhood relationship to the parent was one of healthy respect and admiration, then the relationship to a partner who resembles the parent may be healthy as well.

If the child-parent love was neurotic, and never really severed, the relationship with the replacement partner in adulthood is destined to suffer. The man who marries the girl who resembles his mother may become impotent with her, most often after she becomes a mother herself and more like the "forbidden" mother of childhood. The woman who marries a father figure may, for the same reason, be frigid with her husband, as well as overly dependent and resentful of her dependency. (237)

Some adults still unhealthily attached to their parents are held by hate, not love. Choosing an intimate partner is then part of a rebellion. The partner is chosen not for qualities the chooser appreciates but for qualities the parent will despise. For this reason the son of a preacher will marry a call girl, and the daughter of a teacher will marry a school dropout. The problem in such matings is more than mismatching. The rebelling partner still identifies with his parents and eventually judges his partner as they do. (238)

People, without parental hangups, who marry for love can also come to grief, often because they expect too much of love and of the loved one. They really expect love to make the world go around, in a climate of continual happiness.

Because they expect so much of love, intimate couples often think they can't be too close to each other, and smother their individuality in a struggle toward mutual dependence. When one or another becomes claustrophobic and reverses the struggle in a life-saving maneuver toward independence, the other moves in closer instead of giving the partner breathing space. (239, 240)

The result is hostility on both sides, an emotion that the lovers identify as the antithesis of love. It isn't. Love is a complex combination of emotions that includes within it hostility, hate, envy, anger, and many other feelings we've been taught to deplore.

If we know that all these are a part of love, then we can handle the situation when one of them surfaces. If we don't understand this, then we believe that love dies when confronted by anger, and we either bury love prematurely or bury the unacceptable emotion. In either case love loses. For a relationship that ignores honest antagonisms only builds destructive, explosive components. (241)

Intimate partners who never fight aren't really intimate. They've settled for living side by side rather than together. Partners who live together must constantly make adjustments. And usually only the unimportant adjustments are made without conflict and compromise. (242)

The conflicts are most quickly and effectively resolved if both partners are tactfully honest with each other. The silent partner who expects the other to read his mind doesn't facilitate the settlement of disagreements. Neither does the partner who refuses to thrash things out. (243)

There are also love partners who make conflict a way of life. If there is nothing to quarrel about in the present, one can always dig up old loves so that the other can become jealous of these bygone affairs. Or infidelity can be flaunted to trigger jealousy reactions. (244, 245)

Sex is always a fertile ground for conflict. It can be demanded with hostility and withheld as punishment. More constructively it can be used to bridge the gap between conflict and togetherness. But it can only be used in this way by partners who aren't so hung up on love as a prerequisite for sex that they refuse this resolution of their difficulties. (246)

Even in the best matched partners the desire for sex doesn't always coincide. Neither does the desire for food, recreation, or sleep. Differences in the latter can be taken in stride and accommodations made. Differences in sexual desire are too often taken as a rejection of self by the one who makes the advances. More often they represent inhibitions or fears on the part of the partner. And all too seldom are these examined and resolved. (247, 248)

One of the big fears is unwanted pregnancy. The woman worried about all the things that could go wrong with her birth control measures hasn't much emotion left over to spend on sexual enjoyment. The pregnancy-shy male makes a better detective than lover, with his concern over whether or not his partner has taken her birth control pills. (249)

The well-adjusted couple talks over contraceptive measures outside the bedroom, knows the chances of failure, and plans ahead for mishaps. Having done that, they can make love without fear. And having been realistic in one area of their lovemaking they can be realistic in others. Neither expects his partner, nor himself, to be always in sexual prime. So neither has to project blame for sexual disappointments on the other. Nor feel that sexual incapacity is a reflection on the self. (250)

The realistic couple knows that sex, like anything else in life, has its ups and downs. Neither believes that when sex is down love is dead and intimacy impossible. It's at this time that the intimate couple can offer each other psychological support and nondemanding physical caresses that permit sex to blossom again unhindered.

6: Sexual Behavior

Much of our behavior in new situations is modeled on the observation of others. In a strange community or country we follow the lead of those who know the customs. When we enter the unfamiliar world of sex, however, we proceed without models.

Few intimate partners have ever seen others in sexual congress. Many have never seen the naked body of a person of the opposite sex until the first moment of lovemaking. Yet at that moment

each expects himself and his partner to put in a perfect performance as a lover.

IGNORANCE

Both expect this, though neither is at all sure what is involved
in a perfect performance. Or even whether they are properly
equipped for their roles. Often they have heard tales of the sexual
prowess of others and wonder if they are as sexy. He fears his
penis may be too small. If she is inexperienced she may fear it
will be too large and injure her in some way. (251, 252)

The misinformation most couples bring with them to an initial
sexual rendezvous is staggering. *She,* as well as *he,* may be completely ignorant of the anatomy of the female genitalia or the
process by which the woman comes to orgasm. *She,* as well as
he, may feel that her genitals are not only complicated and mysterious but also unclean.

They may actually be unclean if she has been taught that
to touch there is improper, even when bathing. Men also often
neglect the genitals in favor of scrubbing the armpits. Persons
with such little respect for their own sexual organs are likely to
be repelled as well by those of the opposite sex. (253, 254)

A delightful way for intimate partners to learn to know each
other's bodies and to feel at home with them is to shower or bathe
together. Admiring and being admired, touching and enjoying
each other, get rid of feelings of physical shame and shyness.
Soon all your senses, including your sense of smell and taste, will
add to your delight in your loved one and to your love-making.
(255, 256, 257)

When inexperienced partners wish to express their love physically they are often handicapped by ignorance of the body and
the sexual responses of the opposite sex. Someone who hasn't
come to orgasm through masturbation or petting doesn't even
know what to expect of himself.

The partner in this situation is usually the woman. More than
90 percent of all men have masturbated, and most do so regularly

when they haven't other sexual outlets. This is excellent preparation for intimacy, for both men and women. For the person who knows what pleases him or her sexually can help his partner give sexual pleasure. (258)

And that is what any couple should concern themselves with —pleasure! As they explore the ways they can delight each other sensuously, pleasure mounts and mounts until orgasm happens. That's a lot more pleasure than couples get who concentrate on climax alone. They miss all the fun along the way.

The whole body is sensuously sensitive, but it is stimulation of the penis, for the male, that finally triggers orgasm. Almost all couples know this, even the most inexperienced. What even many experienced couples don't know is that the pleasure center that brings orgasm for the woman is the clitoris, at the very front of the vulva, between the vagina and the hairy mons pubis. The tiny clitoris is the focus of female sexual sensitivity, the equivalent of the penis in the male. In fact, the clitoris is the only organ in the human body whose sole function is sexual pleasure. In its tiny rosebud-sized glans there are approximately as many sexual receptor cells as there are in the head of the male penis. (259, 260, 261)

This makes the clitoris exquisitely sensitive. That's why during masturbation, most women manipulate the area of the vulva around the clitoris, which is also rich in sexual receptor cells as well as in nerves leading to the clitoris. In contrast to the clitoris and the area around it, the vagina has very few sexual cells or nerve endings, and these only at its entrance.

During coitus, stimulation of the clitoris is achieved indirectly. As the penis thrusts within the vagina it moves the vulva's inner lips (labia minora), which are attached to the hood of the clitoris. This causes the hood to rub rhythmically over the glans to produce the sexual excitation that triggers orgasm.

Though we usually think of the genitals as the place where sexual stimulation occurs, nothing happens even there without the cooperation of the mind. It is in the mind that the greatest variations for intimacy potential are found. People who are work-oriented turn off all thoughts of pleasure when there are tasks to be done. If the tasks aren't completed, they are inclined to keep them in the back of their minds even when they seem to be devoting themselves to pleasure. This makes them less receptive to sensual sensation during physical intimacy.

People who often remember or anticipate sexual pleasure with delight during their daily duties are ready to give themselves to the experience completely when they have the opportunity. Most such people report that, far from interfering with their work performance, their occasional erotic thoughts are more refreshing than coffee breaks. (262)

But because they put living ahead of earning a living, these life-oriented persons may very well arrive late to work now and then because they made love in the morning. They enjoy a change in time and place and usually welcome particularly a chance to do what comes naturally in a natural surrounding. (263, 264)

Intimacy means sharing. The person who is only interested in his own physical satisfaction makes a poor intimate partner. So does the person who puts the goal of mutual orgasm ahead of sensuous joy. There's usually not much sharing in mutual orgasm since each partner, blanked out by his own overwhelming sensation, is in no condition to really appreciate the other's climax. (265, 266)

Intimacy isn't fostered either when men follow the advice of experts or peers in order to give their partners more time to come to orgasm. Then they turn their attention on and off to prolong erection and intromission. And sometimes even coat their penises with anesthetizing ointment to make them less sexually sensitive. Unfortunately, the ointment can also anesthetize the genitals of the partner. And nothing is more likely to turn her off than a man who is performing mechanically while his mind is elsewhere. (267, 268)

What the woman often needs instead of time to come to orgasm is greater clitoral stimulation before or during coitus, or both. Since clitoral stimulation is indirect after intromission it is sometimes insufficient, particularly if the male has entered the vagina before the female was fully ready. (269)

This happens because, in our culture, we assume that the male is always a sexual expert who knows best what will please his partner. The couple who will put aside this fiction and instead learn from each other during relaxed sexual play exactly what delights each, are the most apt to experience ecstasy and orgasm for both. (270, 271)

Relaxed sexual play also allows the woman to have more than one orgasm if she is multi-orgasmic, as many women are. These women are not nymphomaniacs; they are healthy, normal women, sexually well endowed. They are often called nymphomaniacs, a derogatory term impossible to define, by people with less sexual capacity. (272)

The time to work toward goals is not during lovemaking but before. Both men and women can increase the pleasure they give their partners, and the strength of their own orgasms, by exercising their genital muscles regularly. This is a simple matter of rhythmically tightening and relaxing the muscles around the vagina or the penis for a brief period several times each day. (273)

To become an active partner in the sexual relationship a woman should understand the male genitalia and sexual reactions so that she can give her lover stimulation, at his direction, just as he gives her pleasure. It is important that she realize that the erection of the penis is not under voluntary control. In long-continued sexual play the erection can subside. Or a distraction, such as a loud noise, or his partner's mention of a non-sexual subject, can cause a man to lose his erection. With proper arousing techniques the erection can be restored. (274)

The woman should realize too that after a certain point of excitation the male cannot control ejaculation. She shouldn't blame him if she has not reached climax. He probably regrets it as much as she does. Neither should she continue sexual stimulation in an attempt to produce another immediate erection in her partner. For some men this can be extremely painful. And after ejaculation all men have a refractory period lasting from a few seconds to a few hours, during which sexual arousal is impossible. (275)

INHIBITIONS

One of the most exciting forms of sex play in which intimate partners indulge is the oral stimulation of the genitals. When the male genitals are caressed in this way it is called fellatio. When the mouth and tongue are applied to the female genitals it is called cunnilingus. Men with erection problems are sometimes able to attain a full engorgement of the penis through fellatio. And women who are nonorgasmic in intercourse can often be brought to climax through cunnilingus. (276)

Though oral-genital contact is often used as part of foreplay only, it can also take the place of intercourse as a way to reach orgasm in recreational sex. It is in every way as natural, normal, proper, and pleasurable as coitus. Since the female does not ejaculate during orgasm the male does not have to worry that an emission will harm him if he brings her to orgasm orally. The male ejaculate is clean, nonfattening, and rich in protein. (277, 278, 279)

Prejudice against oral-genital sex stems from the days when we needed to increase the population and everything but reproductive sex was discouraged. As a result there are laws against the practice in many state and city legal codes. Despite the laws, an estimated 75 percent of married couples engage in oral sex. (280)

Many perfectly normal respectable couples also ignore public prejudice and legal restrictions by engaging in anal sex. There is nothing perverted about anal sex, or about any other sexual practice that both partners desire and enjoy, and that harms no one. (281)

In entering the anus, the male should use both care and lubrication. And he should wear a condom. Though there is no fecal matter in the rectum between evacuations, harmful bacteria can linger there that might infect his urinary tract if it is unprotected. He can also carry infectious bacteria to the vagina if he withdraws from the anus and immediately enters there.

What gives pleasure, not what is proper, should be the criterion for sexual practices and positions. Both are often as rigidly stereotyped as Emily Post's etiquette for a wedding. Thus, in our society, the male-superior, woman-supine position lingers on, a relic from the days when women were supposed to have no interest in sex and were, therefore, pinned immobile on the bed by their subduers. In most of the rest of the world this position is ridiculed as the "missionary" position. The lateral side-by-side position for coitus gives greater freedom of movement to both partners. (282, 283, 284)

Couples who are spontaneous and free in their lovemaking let their own desires, not prejudice and tradition, determine when and where they will enjoy intimate relations. They are adventurous and creative. They eagerly try new times and places and positions to add zest to their sex life. But they don't make the mistake of thinking sex is the whole of physical intimacy. They enjoy contact with each other even in sleep. (285, 286)

MYTHOLOGY

Equally as destructive of sexual enjoyment as our inhibitions are the myths that grow up around sex, like weeds in an untended garden. Strangely, many of these fables involve the most prominent sexual organ of all, the penis. Proving, perhaps, that fantasies can serve our purposes more effectively than observation.

There is, for instance, the widespread belief that a large man has a larger penis than a small man. Actually, the penis has little relation to body size. Just as a small man may have an impressive nose, so he may have a penis of above-average measurements. (287)

Not that penile size makes any difference except in locker rooms, where men with small organs try to hide them behind towels. They have no need to feel inferior. Since the small penis has a greater capacity for expansion, sometimes to double its length, it may well surpass the larger organ in size when erect. (288)

Either organ will give both sexual partners the same amount of stimulation during intercourse, and will fit as tightly into the vagina. That's because the vagina is a potential, rather than an actual, space. It dilates exactly enough to accommodate the organ that enters, so that contact is the same whether the penis is large or small. (289)

Circumcision is also thought by many to affect sexual performance. Since the uncircumcised glans is covered with a foreskin it is believed by some to be less sensitive to sexual stimulation. It is therefore assumed that uncircumcised males can give their partners more time to come to orgasm because they can hold off ejaculation longer. The opposite point of view also obtains—that the circumcised glans is less sensitive, because it is dulled by constant contact with the clothing without the protection of the foreskin.

Tests measuring the sensitivity of the circumcised and uncircumcised glans, however, have failed to reveal any difference in sensitivity between the two. Moreover, in most instances, any difference would be lost in sexual performance because during coition the foreskin retracts from the head of the fully erect penis, leaving the glans exposed, just as it is in the circumcised state. (290)

Another minor operation thought to affect the sexual performance of the male is the vasectomy. This is a male method of birth control in which the ducts that carry the seminal fluid from the testicles to the urethra are severed. The operation does not interfere with the production of sperm but only with distribution. Instead of joining the ejaculatory fluids, the sperm are absorbed by surrounding tissues.

Since sperm compose a very minute part of the ejaculate the volume is not decreased. Neither is the sterilized male rendered less potent, as some believe. Or more potent, as others insist. Only his capacity to reproduce is affected. (291)

A less permanent and more frequent method of male birth control is coitus interruptus, in which the male withdraws from the vagina before ejaculation. This is one of the less effective methods of contraception because it is founded on the fallacy that the male discharges sperm only during ejaculation. But frequently, immediately before orgasm, the man secretes a few drops of mucoid substance that often contain sperm. (292)

Though coitus interruptus is a poor method of birth control, it is a major cause of premature ejaculation. The premature ejaculator's difficulties have been popularly ascribed to excessive masturbation, but Masters and Johnson have found that this is not a cause. Hurried, goal-oriented experiences with prostitutes or with dates in parked cars or behind bushes more often precipitate the trouble. (293)

Untreated, premature ejaculation can develop into impotence. Both can be cured, the first more easily than the latter. Unfortunately, men troubled with these problems try hope and home remedies instead of getting expert help. Usually their efforts only increase the fear of performance that is the major psychological block to effective sexual functioning. (294)

Fear of performance grows greater as men reach middle age. It is then that they begin to fear the impotence they believe will be their fate in later years. To save up their sexual capacity for this period some men drastically curtail their sexual outlets. This is the worst thing they could do. The men who continue sexually active into their seventies and eighties are those who have maintained sexual regularity throughout their lives. (295)

Just as other natural functions continue into the golden years in the healthy adult, so does sexual capacity. When it fails the cause is not age alone but more often psychological conditioning and physical unconditioning. Common causes of sexual incapacity in the aging male are overeating, underexercising, and overindulgence in alcohol. (296, 297)

Age doesn't rob men of sexual desire and ability; nor does it rob women. Neither menopause nor hysterectomy, the surgical removal of the womb, causes sexual incapacity in the female. Quite often, in fact, women's desire for sexual expression increases after the menopause has freed them from concern over pregnancy. (298)

Sex, it seems, is not a capacity reserved for the young. To keep it we have only to use it, with the secure knowledge that we can never use it up. For to those who have learned to enjoy sex as an uninhibited romp rather than as a performance test or a duty, the precious gift will never grow old. And it will help them to stay young all of their lives. (299, 300)

Your Final IPQ

It is now time to calculate your overall Intimacy Potential Quotient. To do this, add the sectional scores you have entered at the end of each section. Divide the sum of these six figures by six. The result is your final percentage score in intimacy—your Intimacy Potential Quotient (IPQ). Enter it in the space provided below.

The highest possible IPQ is 100. No one has ever scored that. And your actual score is less important than how you use your intimacy potential in real life. And how well it matches your partner's.

Keep the record of your IPQ and of your sectional scores to enter on your profile graph in the chapter that follows. Once you have filled in your profile you will be able to see whether or not, over the years, you have been developing or inhibiting your intimacy potential. And by superimposing a partner's profile on your own you will have a clear picture of where you jibe and where you clash.

INTIMACY POTENTIAL QUOTIENT   ——

21
Mating and Mismating

Having completed your IPQ Questionnaire you will want to chart the results in a profile graph so that you can examine your intimacy profile. And you may want to superimpose your intimate partner's profile on your own, as we have done for several partners on the illustrative profiles. Before you make up a graph of your own scores, you may find it helpful to look at the sample profiles in some detail.

In Profile No. 1, on page 262, both Steve and Eve have IPQs of almost 70. Eve was surprised at this. On the basis of what she knew about Steve, and feared about herself, she presumed he would have a much higher IPQ than she and that, therefore, they were mismatched, fond as they were of each other. What she didn't know was that Steve, represented by the solid line, had had a less fortunate childhood than she. He was bottle-fed, little handled, and his toilet training was unbelievably harsh.

During adolescence Steve left home, went to college, and made up his own mind about many things, including sex. So his temperament and attitudes leap upward on the chart. His social and sexual behavior fall below them, because he hasn't yet matched his actions to his ideas. With his attitudes at 90 on the graph he can still be expected, at age thirty-two, to overcome some of his childhood training in body as well as in mind.

Now let's look at Eve, represented by the dotted line. She was a pampered baby, loved and cuddled and adored. At puberty she was ripe for an intimate relationship, but she met an exploi-

IPQ PROFILE NO. 1   STEVE_____EVE_ _

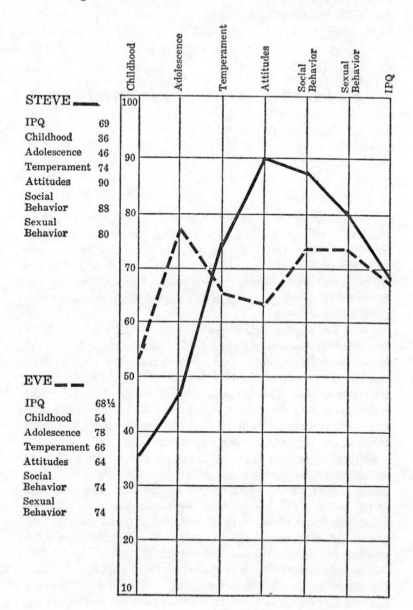

STEVE _____

IPQ	69
Childhood	36
Adolescence	46
Temperament	74
Attitudes	90
Social Behavior	88
Sexual Behavior	80

EVE _ _

IPQ	68⅓
Childhood	54
Adolescence	78
Temperament	66
Attitudes	64
Social Behavior	74
Sexual Behavior	74

tive older male instead. He used her and left her pregnant. Though her parents helped her through an abortion, the experience left scars. For a long time Eve thought she hated sex and she distrusted men.

This shows in the downward swing of her temperament and attitudes. Her fortunate childhood training in intimacy, however, continues to influence her social behavior and her sexual behavior. Still, at this time, at the age of twenty-nine, when she is recovering from her adolescent calamity, another exploitive male could send her IPQ plummeting downward. Luckily Steve is not exploitive, as his profile indicates. For the typical profile of an exploitive male look at Harry's graph (Profile No. 5 on page 269).

So the prognosis for Steve and Eve is good, despite Eve's doubts before they answered the questionnaire. They are matched within two points on their Intimacy Potential Quotient. And both have good intimacy training in their backgrounds—she in childhood and he later. That will stand them in good stead in their intimate relationship.

But let us just suppose that Eve had met Harry, or someone like him. She might well have, for Harry, though fifty-five years old and married, frequents dating bars, in search of younger women to serve as sexual partners. He calls them chicks. Still handsome, and with years of practice in seduction behind him, Harry often finds what he is looking for. The younger women are flattered by the lavish attention of an older and prosperous suitor. Harry "makes out all right," he often brags to the fellows at the club.

Brought up in a period when parents often raised children by the rod and the clock, Harry had an unfortunate childhood, as a look at the solid line on Profile No. 5 will show. He revolted out of his harsh childhood into a sexually superactive adolescence. That it was mostly exploitive is shown by his low scores on temperament, attitudes, and social behavior. He is still sexually active and exploitive, and no match for Eve in intimacy potential.

Even without the age difference, a relationship for Harry and Eve could be destructive. Neither has strong enough temperament and attitudes to help the other overcome background ad-

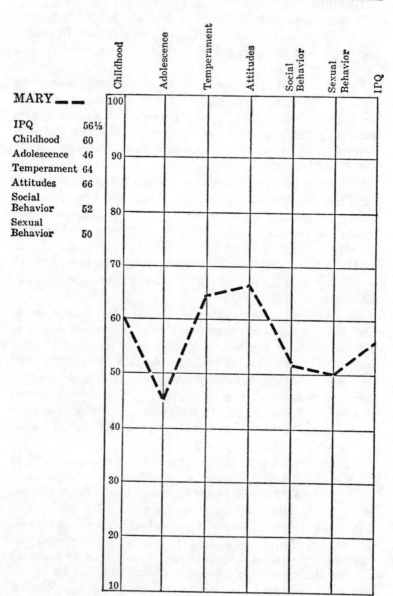

IPQ PROFILE NO. 2   MARY — —

MARY — —

IPQ   56⅓
Childhood   60
Adolescence   46
Temperament   64
Attitudes   66
Social
Behavior   52
Sexual
Behavior   50

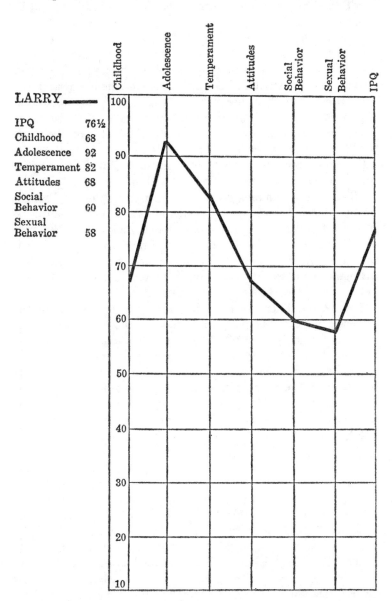

IPQ PROFILE NO. 3   LARRY___

LARRY___

IPQ	76½
Childhood	68
Adolescence	92
Temperament	82
Attitudes	68
Social Behavior	60
Sexual Behavior	58

versities. She would soon begin to feel used and abused and he would wander.

Now let's look at Mary's profile (Profile No. 2). Mary received quite a lot of affection in childhood but, as often happens with girls, it was cut off in her teenage years and her opportunities for intimacy were restricted. Though her temperament and attitudes have risen since then, her behavior still reflects this adolescent experience. With an IPQ of 56⅓ it would appear that she would make an unsatisfactory intimate partner for any of the more highly sexed males on our charts. (Harry would make an unsatisfactory intimate partner for anyone.) But let's compare Mary's profile more closely with Larry's (Profile No. 3).

His is a fairly common profile for a man in his thirties. Brought up by educated, progressive parents he had a better than usual childhood and a free and sexually active adolescence. But note the downward trend of the graph after that. Our young man is no longer interested in intimacy, or even in sex. He's busy making his mark in the world. As a result his score on social and sexual behavior exceeds Mary's by only eight points.

The largest difference in their charts is in the adolescent experience, which is in part a reflection of the difference in the ways we bring up boys and girls. In present sexual behavior these two are fairly close. Since her temperament and attitudes are so much higher than her behavior, we can assume that her behavior still reflects the adolescent restrictions on sex outside marriage. Once a wedding certificate gives her "permission" for sexual expression, her sexual behavior could easily jump the eight points to meet Larry's.

But what's important here is that her sexual behavior doesn't exceed his. She won't make sexual demands on him that he, preoccupied with career, isn't ready to meet. Although his IPQ is higher than hers, closer to Eve's (Profile No. 1), and almost a match for Milly's (Profile No. 4), he would be ill-advised to choose either Eve or Milly as a mate, in view of the fact that his graph shows a falling, rather than a rising, interest in intimacy. And either of them would be ill-advised to choose him.

A declining interest in intimacy can sometimes be lifted by an understanding intimate partner. But this is more apt to hap-

IPQ PROFILE NO. 4   BILLY———MILLY— —

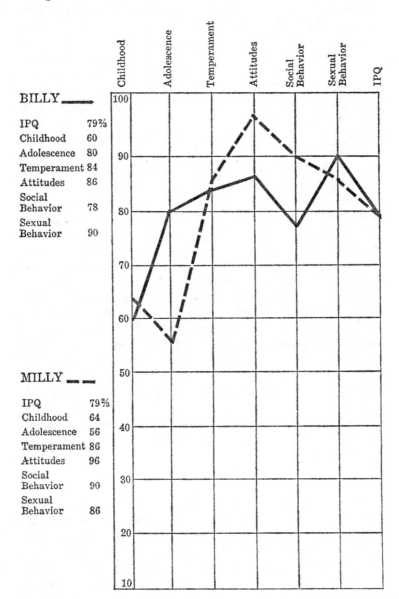

BILLY———

IPQ	79⅔
Childhood	60
Adolescence	80
Temperament	84
Attitudes	86
Social Behavior	78
Sexual Behavior	90

MILLY — —

IPQ	79⅔
Childhood	64
Adolescence	56
Temperament	86
Attitudes	96
Social Behavior	90
Sexual Behavior	86

pen when the reason for the decline is a void in life that intimacy can fill. This void could have been caused by a siege of illness, grief, or loss of a previous intimate partner.

When intimacy has been crowded out of a life by an all-consuming interest in a career, however, even the search for a mate may be motivated by a desire to further the career rather than a desire for intimacy. Then the wish for intimacy on the part of the high-IPQ partner can be resented by the career-oriented partner, and his refusal of affectionate attention can be frustrating to the one who needs greater amounts of intimacy.

Let's look at the profiles of Billy and Milly, he represented by the solid line in Profile No. 4 and she by the broken line. These two are almost ideally matched. Their childhoods were similar and both were above average in intimacy training. Though their adolescent graph points reflect the difference between the teenage experience of boys and girls in our culture, Milly wasn't too severely restrained in these formative years, nor did Billy go wild.

Notice that Billy's temperament and attitude exceed his adolescent sexual behavior, as does his sexual behavior at the time of answering the questionnaire (age twenty-six). Not uncommonly the female's temperament, attitudes, and social behavior exceed the male's, as Milly's exceed Billy's. As an added bonus there is only a four-point difference in their sexual behavior.

At the age of twenty-six, Milly is only beginning to overcome the influence of society's restrictions on adolescent women. She can be expected to peak sexually in the next few years. Billy has also been moving upward on the chart, both psychologically and behaviorally. Their relationship should grow increasingly intimate in the future.

We have already discussed Harry, whose chart is typical of the exploitive sexual jock. Harry is married to Carrie, represented by the broken line on Profile No. 5. Carrie is a pretty but dependent woman who has been forty-six years old several years now and will probably remain the same age for several more.

Through twenty years of marriage and two children she has been nonorgasmic and has spent the past few years looking for the "magic penis" that will awaken her sensuously. It is not uncommon for married women to be unfaithful for the first time in

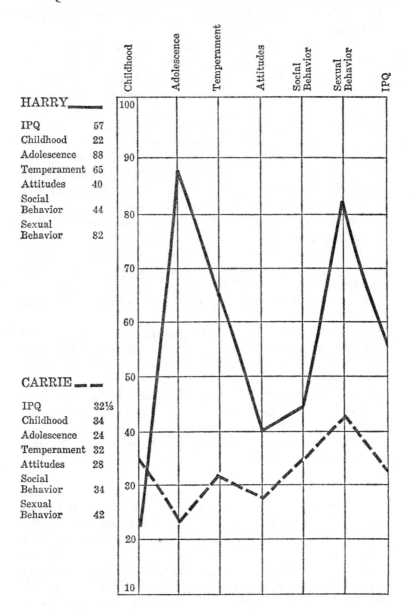

IPQ PROFILE NO. 5   HARRY———CARRIE——

HARRY———

IPQ	57
Childhood	22
Adolescence	88
Temperament	65
Attitudes	40
Social Behavior	44
Sexual Behavior	82

CARRIE—— ——

IPQ	32⅓
Childhood	34
Adolescence	24
Temperament	32
Attitudes	28
Social Behavior	34
Sexual Behavior	42

the menopausal years, to prove to themselves that they are still attractive.

Carrie has had two brief affairs and three one-time-only sexual exposures to men other than her husband. This accounts for the upswing in her sexual behavior on the graph. Despite this recent activity she has not found the magic penis and she is still non-orgasmic.

Notice that her childhood experience with intimacy was below normal and her adolescence unusually restrictive, as was common in the years when Carrie was growing up. Notice also that her sex drive has never been strong enough to pull her upward on the graph. She truly embraced the dependent woman role and expected Harry to be a Prince Charming who would bring her happiness. He didn't, and neither have the other potential rescuers she has tested.

Her husband, Harry, scores high on sexual behavior and low on attitudes and social behavior. These two peaks, one at adolescence and one at sexual behavior, are indicators of a sexual performer rather than someone interested in the personality of his partner.

Men like Harry frequently marry "good" girls, like Carrie, who have low sexual needs. That's because the Harrys of this world still cling to the double standard, left over from caveman days when men had to subdue their mates. They believe that men are by nature sexually aggressive and active, but that truly feminine women are really "above all that" and only submit to sex to oblige the men who have won them.

This attitude puts a strain on the marital relationship. So does the difference in sex drives and the dependence of the submissive mate who waited to be won. She wants someone to bring her ecstasy. He thinks she shouldn't even desire it. In an effort not to "humiliate" her too frequently by subjecting her to his sexual needs, he increasingly searches for sexual outlets outside the marriage and increasingly finds her less interesting as a bed partner.

This can put him in a real psychological bind. He feels guilty about betraying her, and spending so much time away from her. But he also feels guilty because he's humiliating her when he stays home and makes love to her, and because he finds her less exciting than his other sexual partners. Very often his subconscious tries to solve his dilemma by causing him to develop selective impotence. Though perfectly capable with his girl friends, he finds he can no longer make love to his wife. Since he prides himself on his sexuality this causes him a good deal of anguish, which doesn't help his potency.

Unfortunately we are still bringing up males like Harry, who regard women as sexual objects, and females like Carrie who depend on sexual attraction to capture a man to depend on for everything else. People who use other people are incapable of intimacy.

Compatibility

It is one of the common myths about sex that everybody has the same capacity, or ought to have. Though no one is quite sure just what this capacity should be, everyone is worried whether he or she, in comparison with others, is oversexed or undersexed. To be undersexed would be a reflection on his manhood or her femininity. To be oversexed might mean that he was afflicted with satyriasis or she with nymphomania. Both of these diseases are imaginary products of our cultural fear of sex. Neither has ever been adequately defined or reliably diagnosed.

In fact, it is impossible to be oversexed or undersexed except in relationship to a particular partner. People differ in sex drive just as they differ in height, body build, energy levels, and intelligence. Nobody ever has to tell the college boy that if he wants a tennis partner he will have to pick someone whose interest in the game, and potential ability to play it, matches his own. Or that if he wants an intellectual companion he will have to choose someone whose intelligence and interests are similar to his.

He understands these things. But he often fails to use the same reasoning when it comes to sex because he has been misled into

COMPATIBILITY PROFILE

Rate yourself between the two extremes on a scale of 10.
Then superimpose your intimate partner's rating
to find out how compatible you are.

	0	2	4	6	8	10	
I want to be free.							I want marriage and fidelity.
No children for me.							I want a large family.
I am a school dropout.							I have a Ph.D.
I am often ill.							I am always healthy.
I am an atheist.							I am very religious.
I am a spendthrift.							I am a miser.
I am a neatnik.							I am sloppy.
I am an optimist.							I am a pessimist.
I am moody.							I am always cheerful.

COMPATIBILITY PROFILE (continuing)

	0	2	4	6	8	10	
I am a day person.							I am a night person.
I like to live in the city.							I like to live in the country.
I am a daredevil.							I am cautious.
I am a social climber.							I am nonsocial.
I am nonpolitical.							I am politically involved.
I am informal.							I am formal.
I love a crowd.							I like to be alone.
I like to watch TV.							TV bores me.
I like open windows.							I like a warm house.
I am a homebody.							I like to travel.
I like posh hotels.							I like to camp out.

believing that there are "normally" sexed people and "abnor-
mally" sexed people, and that with a little consideration for each
other any two normal people can make a sexual adjustment. The
facts are otherwise, as any marriage counselor knows too well.

The man or woman who wants sex only every other week is
going to have a hard time accommodating a partner who desires
intercourse twice a day. Indeed, there's going to be more recrim-
ination than accommodation, with each accusing the other of
being oversexed or undersexed. Each is quite normal, just as a
five-foot person and a six-foot person are both normal. And each
would be quite happy with a partner whose sexual desires
matched his own.

Given such a partner, both the highly sexed person and the
one with a lower sex drive would have an excellent chance of
developing a satisfying intimate relationship. Mismatched sexual
partners can rarely do this, however, because anxiety and hostility
block both emotional and physical contact.

If you and your prospective partner, or partners, have answered the questionnaire honestly (instead of trying to "up-
grade" your scores), then studying your profiles, superimposed
one on the other, should give you a pretty good idea of how physically compatible you are. Naturally, you'll take into account what
you know of each other as well. But what you'll learn from the
questionnaire and the profiles, particularly if you discuss them,
will be a lot more than you would learn from a weekend, or even
several weekends, spent together.

Sexual incompatibility isn't the only thing that can destroy a
relationship, of course. Differences large and small can work
against intimacy. If he rises with the sun and whistles in the
shower, while she yearns for more sleep, this "day" person and
"night" person aren't going to be very compatible in the morning.
Nor will they be compatible in the evening, either, when he re-
tires at eight just as she is beginning to come awake.

To test yourself and potential partners in the most frequent
areas of domestic discord, fill out the Compatibility Profile, rating
yourself and letting your partner rate himself on a scale from 0
to 10 between the extremes listed at the bottom and the top of
the scale. For instance, if you are the night person we just de-

scribed you would place a dot at 10, just below "I am a night person." If your partner is strictly a day person, he would place his mark at 0, just above "I am a day person." If, on the other hand, he is the flexible kind of soul who can adjust to getting up early when necessary, or staying up late when there's a reason to do so, he would place himself at around 5, in the middle of the scale.

Do this with all the extremes listed and compare your placements. Some of the differences that show up will be minor and subject to compromise. Slophounds can learn to be more tidy and neatniks can train themselves to put up with a little disorder. Other differences will have to be lived with, if this partner is going to be lived with. Throughout the years there will be times when the person who believes in fidelity will seem possessive, jealous, and confining to the partner who likes to play the field. And he will seem callous, unloving, and cruel to his faithful partner.

It may be hard to face possibilities like this at the beginning of a relationship. But that's the time when differences that may erode intimacy should be faced. Difficult as it is to decide before the fact that a partnership won't work out, it's a good deal easier than realizing, after the fact, that it hasn't worked out, and picking up the pieces.

But those who often benefit most from taking the IPQ Questionnaire and establishing their IPQ and Compatibility Profiles are those who find that they are well matched and ready for an intimate relationship, and those who are already intimate. For in answering and discussing the questions, and recognizing their areas of incompatibility, they have learned about themselves and each other, about the strengths their partnership can have, and its weaknesses, potential or actual. And they have faced and discussed differences that, unexplored, could become disruptive. Intimacy thrives best in a soil that has been thoroughly prepared.

Epilogue:
Intimacy in the Future

The future is tomorrow. Some of the changes that will affect our most intimate relationships are just around the corner and others are brightly visible on the horizon. All of them may be summed up by saying that in the future we will have more choices.

The burdens of reproduction will be lifted from our sexual relations. The Pill and fears of overpopulation have already done this to some extent. New contraceptives and abortifacients will give a choice of several reliable methods of birth control. Accidental pregnancy and the miseries it often causes will belong to the past.

So will the unfulfilled desire for a child of one's own. For those who can't or don't wish to reproduce, sperm and ova banks will permit the incubation of a healthy, chosen-to-order fertilized egg, whether within the mother or within a test tube. Women will be able to have children without a nine-month pregnancy, and men, if they want, can have families without marrying women.

What will this do to marriage? It will change it. We will have choices in our family relationships too. We are already making them, and changing marriage as we do so. For the patriarchal, lifelong, monogamous marriage we inherited from our agricultural past wasn't tailored to meet present needs.

This form of marriage originated when a large family was an

economic asset and a wife and children were part of the farming man's chattel, as well as his labor supply. Later, this family arrangement provided a cheap and plentiful source of labor for early industrialization.

In our highly mobile machine age, however, the large family has become an economic and social liability. Its size has been pared not only by reducing the number of offspring but also by eliminating the old, the disabled, and single adults, many of whom have become society's responsibilities.

No longer shackled to maternity, women have become economically independent, cutting the ties that once bound provider and provided-for. Marriage has ceased to be a matter of finance and has become a matter of romance. Men and women marry because they are in love and divorce when love fails.

Marriage to one partner for a lifetime has now become a choice, not a necessity. Many choose successive partners for varying periods of time. What form the marriage will take has also become a matter over which people are exercising free choice. The man may be the head of the household under the law, but for many couples this is a repugnant anachronism. They prefer a democratic marriage between equal partners. And they are also making their own decisions as to whether or not their union means "renouncing all others."

While these changes are taking place within marriage, other living arrangements are being tested outside the legally recognized state of wedlock. Perhaps the most significant of these are the many communes with their different types of interpersonal relationships. These resemble the extended families of the past, except that their common bond is not blood but friendship, or religion, or life style.

Some communes consist of monogamous couples. Others are group marriages in which partners are interchangeable. In some sexual relationships are varied and temporary. There are single-sex communes, with and without homosexual activity. And some religious communes discourage sex except for reproductive purposes. The only thing that all communes seem to have in common, investigators find, is happy children.

Legal marriage today still reflects the view that any sexual union is primarily for reproductive purposes. But people are sexual beings and they need intimate relationships with other people. If they are excluded from these by the law they will seek them outside the law. Today young couples live together openly without benefit of clergy. So do many homosexuals. So do the old, who are often penalized financially by our social security laws if they marry.

These extra-legal alliances are forcing changes in social attitudes and in the law. In the world of tomorrow the many different forms that marriage can take may be legally recognized, and marriage itself may become but one of many socially sanctioned choices for fulfilling sexual and intimacy drives.

When this is true, society will be strengthened, as it always is when it meets the requirements of its members. Morality will be reinforced as it recognizes the claims of biology and the diversity of individuals. And life will be enriched as people are encouraged to develop and express their caring natures through intimacy.

Glossary

A

ABORTION   Removal or expulsion of the fetus before viability, which occurs at the twenty-fourth week of pregnancy. Spontaneous abortions (or miscarriages) are thought to occur in at least one out of every ten pregnancies as a result of inherent defects of the fetus. Voluntary abortions, or induced abortions, are those in which an active role of some agent is effected to obtain this result. Since there is no definition of *life* or *fetal rights,* such procedures may be considered an extension of nature's own fetal wastage.

ADRENALIN   Chemical manufactured by the medulla of the adrenal gland in response to sympathetic nervous action in the fight or flight response.

AMENORRHEA   Cessation of regular menstrual flow. An indication —not a guarantee—of pregnancy.

ANDROGEN   Male sex hormones, often used synonymously with testosterone.

APHRODISIACS   Foods, spices, and drugs reputed to have sexually stimulating powers. Few exist, and none are completely safe.

ARMOR, MUSCULAR   Tight chest and backward-tilted pelvis manifested as a result of anti-sexual conditioning. Identified by Wilhelm Reich.

ARTERIOLES   Blood vessels smaller than arteries and larger than capillaries. They carry blood to organs of the body.

ASPIRATION, VACUUM   A technique for safe and speedy removal of the fetus that utilizes a negative pressure to remove the conceptus from the uterus. This had been done many thousands of times without difficulty and is probably the safest method of voluntary abortion when performed by a qualified practitioner.

ATROPHY Deterioration of a part of the body (including the mind) as a result of withholding activity from that part. Causes a failure of functional ability. Synonymous with senility, sexual failure, hormonal lack, and other diseases thought to be connected with old age. *Old age* is not a disease as such; the conditions related to it are caused almost entirely by disuse and neglect. Prevention of atrophy can often be accomplished through personal attention to health.

AUTONOMIC NERVOUS SYSTEM The automatically functioning part of our internal circuit; once thought to be incapable of voluntary control.

B

BARTHOLIN'S GLANDS Mucus-secreting pockets located at the entrance to the vagina.

BESTIALITY Sexual acts, including intercourse, with animals. According to Kinsey, 17 percent of the American rural male population practices bestiality; the practice is less prevalent (about 7 percent) among urban males.

BION A living being. Also the energy form of the orgone, according to Wilhelm Reich.

BIRTH CONTROL Regulation or prevention of pregnancy.

BISEXUAL Participating in both homosexual and heterosexual relationships.

BROAD LIGAMENT The tissue on either side of the uterus that holds it in position and carries its blood supply.

C

CARUNCLE A small red eminence on the urinary meatus, or opening, in women, which is evidence of an infection of this area. Usually extremely painful, but easily corrected.

CASTRATION Loss, usually surgical, of the gonads—ovaries or

testes. Hormonal replacement therapy can keep individuals thus deprived from sexual atrophy.

CENTRAL NERVOUS SYSTEM The most recently evolved part of the brain, which controls thoughts and the actions of the large muscles of the body.

CEREBELLUM Part of the "old" brain; concerned with the coordination of movements.

CERVICITIS An inflammation of the entrance to the uterus.

CERVIX The mouth of the womb; the part of the uterus lying within the vagina.

CHANCRE A small papule that erodes into a saucer-shaped ulcer.

CIRCUMCISION Removal of the prepuce, or fold of skin, covering the glans clitoris or glans penis.

CLIMACTERIC An end of feminine reproductive ability due to the cessation of cyclic hormonal production. In males, a reduction of androgen production. The symptoms can be major when sexual atrophy has occurred, unnoticeable when it has not been allowed to occur.

CLITORIS Female erotic organ. The only purely sexual organ in the human body.

COCCYX Final curved bone of the spinal column—the tailbone.

COITUS The act of sexual intercourse.

COLOSTRUM First liquid produced by the breasts after childbirth, frequently denied to infants who are born in a hospital environment, which separates mother and child immediately after birth.

COMPULSION An overwhelming, irrational need to do or not to do some particular act. A form of neurotic behavior.

CONDOM A penile sheath made of rubber or animal intestines, designed to protect against venereal infection and/or to prevent pregnancy. It is an inefficient contraceptive device, but it is fairly dependable as a safeguard against VD.

CONDYLOMA ACUMINATA (See wart, venereal).

CORONA GLANDIS The point at which the shaft of the penis meets the glans; the area where pressure using the bioloop should be applied.

CORTEX, ADRENAL   The area where the hormones for life and sex maintenance are produced.

CORTEX, CEREBRAL   The logical and rational front part of the brain.

COWPER'S GLAND   Either of two mucus-secreting glands that discharge into the male urethra.

CREMASTERIC   The nerve that regulates the tension of the cremaster muscle, which raises and lowers the testes according to the warmth of the environment. It also acts reflexively.

CUNNILINGUS   Oral stimulation of the cunnus, or vulva.

CURETTAGE   Scraping of the interior of a cavity and removal of substances with a flattened, sharp spoon. See also D & C.

CYSTITIS   Inflammation of the urinary bladder.

CYSTOCELE   Protrusion of the urinary bladder into the vagina because of muscle weakness or tears. Frequently the result of obstetric trauma; easily corrected surgically.

D

D & C   Dilatation and curettage; the dilating of the cervix, or mouth of the womb, and the scraping out of the lining of the uterus. Often done as a gynecologic diagnostic procedure and occasionally as an effective but somewhat hazardous abortion method.

DARTOS   Muscular tissue within the scrotum.

DEFLORATION   Removal of the hymen—accidentally, surgically, by dilatation, or in intercourse.

DIABETES MELLITUS   A disease that interferes with the body's ability to handle sugar and fat. The more research that is done in this disease the less is known, for it's tremendously complex. It is somehow related to excess weight, but nobody knows whether diabetes causes obesity or vice versa. It does cause serious problems for at least six million Americans, including impotence and other forms of sexual failure.

DIAPHRAGM 1.   Any large muscle that goes from one side of the body to the other.

(a) Abdominal diaphragm, the tentlike muscle between the lungs and the abdomen, usually called simply "diaphragm."

(b) Pelvic diaphragm, the pubococcygeus muscle.

DIAPHRAGM 2. A contraceptive device that consists of a hemisphere of thin rubber held in place (hopefully) by a circular ring at its outer diameter.

DILDO A phallus-shaped device. Used by both men and women, but rarely productive of pleasant vaginal sensations because most of these devices do not stimulate the clitoris.

DOUCHE A bath of the vagina, usually unnecessary. When chemicals are used, this sensitive membrane may be hurt, scarred, and damaged. Douching should only be done on a doctor's prescription.

DYSPAREUNIA Painful intercourse; can occur to males and females alike.

E

EJACULATION The controllable reflex act by which a male emits semen, forcibly, at the same time experiencing orgasm.

ELECTROENCEPHALOGRAPH A recording of the electrical potential changes within the brain by amplification and written or visual display.

EMBRYO The result of conception. No determination has yet been made of the point when an embryo acquires human qualities. Varying philosophies, even within the same religion, hold quite opposing views about this subject. Biology is not able to offer any certainty.

EMPATHY The quality of understanding and appreciating the deep feelings of another.

ENDOCRINE GLANDS Glands of internal secretion. Organized units of body cells that produce specific and potent chemicals and put them in the blood stream for effects in other parts of the body.

EPIDIDYMIS The long cordlike structure along the back wall of the testes, in which sperm are stored.

EPISIOTOMY An incision, usually made with scissors, that enlarges the vaginal opening for obstetric delivery. This is a simple preventive practice needed in nearly all women having their first child, and in most having subsequent births. It preserves the musculature of the vaginal canal by preventing tears.

EROGENOUS ZONES Those areas of the body that are highly supplied with superficial nerve endings and respond to minimal stimulation with feelings of sensuality and sexuality.

F

FELLATIO An oral contact with the penis, considered highly stimulating.

FOREPLAY The period of body contact that precedes coitus.

FRENULUM A bridle of skin that keeps an organ from full movement. Examples are the thin bit of tissue found at the center base of the tongue and that found in a similar position on the penis.

FRIGIDITY An awkward, inaccurate term for undeveloped orgasmic potential in a woman.

G

GONADS The germinal or reproductive tissues of the body. In females these are the ovaries; in males, the testes.

H

HETEROSEXUAL An individual who confines sexual activities to members of the opposite gender.

HOMOPHILE An unflattering and biased term for an individual who has sexual contacts with members of his own sex.

HOMOSEXUAL An individual who confines sexual activities to members of his own gender. The word usually causes more guilt feelings than the word *homophile*. It is not an abnormal behavior, although homosexual acts are often illegal.

HORMONES Chemicals produced by the endocrine glands to maintain the economy of the body.

HOT FLASHES Symptoms of the climacteric that are felt in women suffering from sexual atrophy.

HYMEN   The membrane that occludes the entrance to the vagina. Also known as the guardian of the gate, the cherry.

HYMENECTOMY   Surgical removal of the hymen.

HYSTERECTOMY   Removal of the uterus, often with removal of the ovaries as well.

HYSTERIC-DEPENDENT   A personality that desires unreal goals and seeks to have them fulfilled in a magical manner.

I

INSEMINATION   The deposition of semen into the vagina.

INTROITUS   The entrance to the vaginal canal.

INTROMISSION   Placing the penis within the vagina.

IUD   Intrauterine contraceptive device. A usually effective contraceptive device that dates back at least to the 1800s.

K

KAREZZA   (Coitus reservatus, Oneida method, *Zugassant*) A prolonged, slow, gentle, nearly motionless form of coitus. The ultimate caring caress in which each partner becomes fully aware of the sensual joys of this act.

L

LABIA MAJORA   Large external lips of the vulva, homologous to the scrotum of the male. These may, or may not, be sensitive to erotic stimulation—great individual variations exist.

LABIA MINORA   Inner lips of the vulva, analogous to the shaft of the penis in their origin, and, like it, capable of filling with blood, enlarging, erecting.

LACTATION   Production of milk in the breast. This can be due to pregnancy, even if aborted, or suckling stimulation even without pregnancy—the secret of the wet nurse. Adoptive mothers who have never been pregnant themselves have found that the suckling stimulation of their newly acquired babies was sufficient to produce an adequate and sufficient flow of milk.

LESBIAN   A female homosexual.

LEUKORRHEA   The "whites." Any vaginal discharge. Since this can be vaginal secretion from sexual stimulation it is often not indicative of any disease whatsoever. If heavy, or colored white or green, or bubbly, it indicates the presence of infection and medical advice is needed.

LIBIDO   Sex drive, an inherent part of any organism that undergoes sexual reproduction.

M

MONS PUBIS, VENERIS   The rounded fleshy portion over the pubic bone—symphysis—that is sexually responsive, in both sexes, to stimulation.

N

NYMPHOMANIAC   An imaginary female with an insatiable desire for coitus. Heightened sexual desire frequently occurs in nonorgasmic women, but this is not the problem used as plot material by uninformed writers.

O

OOPHORECTOMY   Removal of the ovaries.

ORGASM   Intense, paroxysmal, emotional, and sexual excitement, followed by the sudden release of physical and psychic tension.

ORGONE   An unproven postulate of Wilhelm Reich, a vital energy that pervades nature and can be accumulated for human use by sitting in a specially designed box.

ORIFICE   Any bodily opening.

OSTEOMALACIA   A softening of the bone characteristic of estrogen-deprived adult women. The four major causes of hospitalization for women over sixty are fractures of various kinds, all directly attributable to estrogen deficiency.

OVULATION   The production, by the ovary, of an egg; accompanied by the presence of other endocrine changes that promote pregnancy.

P

"PAP" SMEAR Named for George M. Papanicolaou, M.D., who discovered that many cancers could be detected early by studying individual cells in smears taken from areas of the body: cervix, uterus, stomach, lungs, etc.

PEDERASTY Forced anal intercourse between mature and young males. Practiced and glorified by many ancient philosophers and writers upon whom we rely for much of our guidance. Even today this term is a source of confusion. It is often equated with male homosexuality in popular writings.

PENIS The male sexual organ.

PERINEUM The anatomical area between the mons pubis and the anus.

PESSARY Any device inserted within the vagina, or cervix, for a variety of purposes.

PHALLUS A synonym for penis.

PHIMOSIS A tightness of the prepuce that prevents it from being drawn back over the glans penis or clitoris.

PORNOGRAPHY Any visual or written depiction of sexual parts or activity that is not considered to have "redeeming social value."

PREMATURE EJACULATION Defined on the East Coast as ejaculation less than sixty seconds after intromission, on the West Coast as ejaculation less than thirty seconds after intromission—or is it the other way around? Realistically, an inability of the male to control the duration of erection prior to orgasm.

PROGESTERONE The female sex hormone that increases within the body from the middle of the menstrual cycle, and whose diminution causes menstruation, in part. A necessary chemical in oral birth control tablets.

PROMISCUOUS Sexually undiscriminating. When applied to the sexual behavior of another, it usually indicates more activity than the speaker deems proper.

PROSTATE A gland which in the male surrounds the neck of the bladder and the urethra. It is made up partly of glandular matter, the ducts from which empty into the urethra, and partly of muscular fibers which encircle the urethra.

PROSTITUTION   The bartering of sexual favors.

PSYCHOSOMATIC   An awkward word, coined in 1936, to try to help us overcome the Puritan dichotomy of body and mind. Each person is in fact a oneness; body and mind are only terms, verbal dissections, rather than expressions of reality.

PUBOCOCCYGEUS MUSCLE   The pelvic diaphragm, a broad band of muscle that lies within the bony pelvis and exerts a degree of control in sexual bioloops.

R

RAPE   Forcible intercourse often accompanied by sadistic injury. Also, intercourse illegal because of legal age barriers and inability to give legal consent for the physical act.

REFRACTORY PERIOD   A rest period in the normal cycle of response action. An inevitable period of functional failure is part of natural physiology, and the inherent reason why our bodies cannot engage in sexual overindulgence.

S

SAFF PERIOD   That point in the menstrual cycle during which a woman in her childbearing years is considered incapable of being impregnated.

SATYRIASIS   Nymphomania in the male, another invention of desperate authors.

SEXUAL INADEQUACY   An inability, usually psychic, to participate in full and prolonged coitus.

SMEGMA   The accumulation of cellular tissue between the foreskin and the glans, which must be removed or it will cause painful adhesions and phimosis.

SOIXANTE-NEUF   (French for 69) Simultaneous cunnilingus and fellatio.

SPERMICIDE   A chemical agent, jelly or foam, designed to cause the death of sperm and prevent unwanted pregnancy.

SPHINCTER   A ringlike band of muscles that encloses, and wholly or partly controls, the opening of a natural body orifice.

STERILIZATION The elimination of the possibility of pregnancy through use of chemicals, surgery, or mechanical devices.

STEROID The class name for the body hormones, including sex hormones.

SYMPATHETIC NERVOUS SYSTEM A part of the brain and spinal cord which is in charge of the life-sustaining automatic body processes. Subject to varying degrees of voluntary control.

SYNDROME A set of symptoms which occur together, usually indicating a disorder whose specific cause was unknown at the time of first description.

T

TAMPON A sponge or plug used to absorb body secretions, particularly menstrual flow.

TESTICLE The male gonad.

TRANSVESTISM Wearing the clothes of the opposite sex, no longer considered to be peculiar to those with homophile inclinations.

TUMESCENCE The filling of erectile tissue with blood as a result of excitement.

V

VAGINA The birth canal; the space, lined with mucous membrane and surrounded by muscle, into which the penis enters.

VAGINAL LUBRICATION The "sweating" or secretion of the vagina during sexual arousal and excitement.

VAGINISMUS A spasm of the vaginal musculature, frequently sufficiently severe to prevent penile penetration.

VASECTOMY The surgical interruption of the vas deferens to achieve sterilization, a minor operation.

VASOCONGESTION The filling of any area of the body with slow-flowing blood.

VESTIBULE The space between the labia minora into which the vagina opens.

VULVA The female sexual organ, including the labia majora, labia minora, entrance to the vagina, and clitoris with its prepuce.

W

WART, VENEREAL A specific virus infection that occurs only within the genital area and has been demonstrated to cause cancer of the cervix. Easily transmissible between intimate partners by sexual contact. One of the earlier scientific demonstrations that some cancers, at least, are caused by virus infections.

Bibliography

Alexander, Franz. *Psychosomatic Medicine*. New York: W. W. Norton & Company, 1950.

Bach, George R., and Peter Wyden. *The Intimate Enemy: How to Fight Fair in Love and Marriage*. New York: William Morrow and Company, 1969.

Beach, Frank A. *Sex and Behavior*. New York: John Wiley & Sons, 1965.

Beauvoir, Simone de. *The Second Sex*. New York: Alfred A. Knopf, 1953.

Bergler, Edmund. *The Revolt of the Middle-Aged Man*. New York: Hill & Wang, 1954.

Berne, Eric. *Sex in Human Loving*. New York: Simon & Schuster, 1970.

———. *Transactional Analysis in Psychotherapy*. New York: Grove Press, 1970.

Brecher, Edward and Ruth, eds. *An Analysis of Human Sexual Response*. Boston: Little, Brown and Company, 1966.

Calderone, Mary. *Release from Sexual Tensions*. New York: Random House, 1960.

Dickinson, Robert L. *Human Sex Anatomy*. 2d ed. Baltimore: The Williams & Wilkins Company, 1949.

Ellis, Albert. *The American Sexual Tragedy.* New York: Lyle Stuart, 1962.

———. *Sex without Guilt.* New York: Grove Press, 1965.

———, and Albert Abarbanel, eds. *The Encyclopedia of Sexual Behavior.* 2d ed. New York: Hawthorn Books, 1967.

Friedan, Betty. *The Feminine Mystique.* New York: W. W. Norton & Company, 1963.

Fromme, Allan. *The Ability to Love.* North Hollywood, Calif.: Wilshire Book Company, 1963.

Goldman, George D., and Donald S. Milman, eds. *Modern Woman, Her Psychology and Sexuality.* Springfield, Ill.: Charles C Thomas, 1969.

Harris, Thomas A. *I'm OK—You're OK: A Practical Guide to Transactional Analysis.* New York: Harper & Row, 1969.

Hastings, Donald W. *A Doctor Speaks on Sexual Expression in Marriage.* Boston: Little, Brown and Company, 1966.

Hays, H. R. *The Dangerous Sex.* New York: G. P. Putnam's Sons, 1964.

Horney, Karen. *Feminine Psychology.* Edited by Harold Kelman. New York: W. W. Norton & Company, 1967.

Kama Sutra of Vatsyayana. 1936. Reprint. New York: Medical Press, 1962.

Kinsey, Alfred C., and others. *Sexual Behavior in the Human Male.* Philadelphia: W. B. Saunders Company, 1948.

———. *Sexual Behavior in the Human Female.* Philadelphia: W. B. Saunders Company, 1953.

Larks, Saul David. *Electrohysterography: The Electrical Activity of the Human Uterus in Pregnancy and Labor.* Springfield, Ill.: Charles C Thomas, 1960.

Lewinsohn, Richard. *A History of Sexual Customs.* New York: Harper & Row, 1958.

Linner, Birgitta, in collaboration with Richard J. Litell. *Sex and Society in Sweden.* New York: Pantheon Books, 1967.

Lowen, Alexander. *Betrayal of the Body.* New York: The Macmillan Company, 1966.

——. *Pleasure.* New York: Coward-McCann, 1970.

Luthe, Wolfgang, ed. *Autogenic Training: A Psychophysiologic Approach in Psychotherapy.* 2 vols. New York: Grune & Stratton, 1969.

Maginnis, Patricia, and Lana Clark Phelan. *The Abortion Handbook.* Los Angeles, Calif.: Contact Books, 1969.

Masters, William H., and Virginia E. Johnson. *Human Sexual Response.* Boston: Little, Brown and Company, 1966.

——. *Human Sexual Inadequacy.* Boston: Little, Brown and Company, 1970.

May, Rollo. *Love and Will.* New York: W. W. Norton & Company, 1969.

Mead, Margaret. *Male and Female.* New York: William Morrow and Company, 1949.

Millett, Kate. *Sexual Politics.* New York: Doubleday and Company, 1970.

Montagu, Ashley. *The Natural Superiority of Women.* Rev. ed. New York: The Macmillan Company, 1968.

——. *Sex, Man and Society.* New York: G. P. Putnam's Sons, 1969.

Perls, Fritz. *Ego, Hunger and Aggression: The Beginning of Gestalt Therapy.* New York: Random House, 1969.

Phelan, Nancy, and Michael Volin. *Sex and Yoga.* New York: Harper & Row, 1968.

Pomeroy, Wardell, and John Tebbel. *Boys and Sex*. New York: Delacorte Press, 1968.

———. *Girls and Sex*. New York: Delacorte Press, 1969.

Raab, Wilhelm, ed. *Prevention of Ischemic Heart Disease: Principles and Practice*. Springfield, Ill.: Charles C Thomas, 1966.

Reich, Wilhelm. *The Discovery of the Orgone*. New York: Farrar, Straus & Giroux, 1942.

———. *The Function of the Orgasm*. New York: Farrar, Straus & Giroux, 1961.

Reik, Theodor. *Of Love and Lust*. New York: Farrar, Straus & Giroux, 1956.

———. *The Search Within: The Inner Experiences of a Psychoanalyst*. New York: Farrar, Straus & Giroux, 1956.

Rogers, Carl R., and Barry Stevens. *Person to Person: The Problem of Being Human*. Lafayette, Calif.: Real People Press, 1967.

Rubin, Isadore. *Sexual Life after Sixty*. New York: Basic Books, 1965.

Schutz, William C. *Joy: Expanding Human Awareness*. New York: Grove Press, 1967.

Simeons, A. T. *Man's Presumptuous Brain*. New York: E. P. Dutton and Company, 1960.

Wahl, William C., ed. *Sexual Problems: Diagnosis and Treatment in Medical Practice*. New York: The Free Press, 1961.

Watts, Alan W. *Nature, Man and Woman*. New York: Pantheon Books, 1958.

Winokur, George, ed. *Determinants of Human Sexual Behavior: Fourth Conference on Community Mental Health Research*. Springfield, Ill.: Charles C Thomas, 1963.

The Journal of Sex Research. Published by the Society for the Scientific Study of Sex, 138 East 94th Street, New York, N.Y.

Sexology Magazine. 160 West 14th Street, New York, N.Y.

Index

A

Abortifacient, IUD as, 17
Abortion
  criminal, deaths due to, 48
  IUD causing, 17
Acromegaly, 24
Adhesions, 58, 65
Adolescence
  confusion of sex and love in, 47–48
  cultural restrictions on sexuality during, 195, 266, 270
  exposure to pornography in, 45–46
  IPQ, calculating, 186
  marriage in, 47
  personal relations during, 196–197
  questionnaire, 181–186
  role playing in, 5
  sexual exploitation in, 201
  sexuality during, 195, 198–201
  sterile period in, 18–19
Age
  at marriage, 27
  and sexual ability, 168, 259–260
Alcohol
  abuse, and inability to communicate, 221
  effect on sexual capacity, 66
Alexander, Franz, 217
Alienation, feeling of, 192
Allergies, causing painful intercourse, 59
Alpha waves, 81
  producing, 83–84
Ambisexuality, see Bisexuality

Anal intercourse, 28, 256
Androgen, 14
  in climacteric, 167
  functions of, 14
Anger
  buried and denied, 100
  constructive use of, 162–163, 250
  independent person, 219
  and downward intimacy spiral, 160–161
  expelling through exercise, 101
  expressing, 162–163
  illogical, 163
Animals
  sex play, 30–31
  sexual congress with, 35
Antibiotic prophylaxis, in venereal disease, 61
Anxiety
  and impotence, 259
  about male and female attributes, 192–193
  male, and wish to be female, 20
  toilet training, carried into adulthood, 189
Arm wrestling, 104
Athlete, sexual, 1–2, 229
Attitudes, 223
  toward life, 223
  toward opposite sex, 226–227
  questionnaire, 208–212
  toward self, 224
  toward sex, 225–226, 227–230
Autoeroticism, see Masturbation
Autonomic nervous system, 68–69
  learning control over, 84–85
  sections of, 84–85

B

Bach, George R., 163
Balanitis, 62
Bartell, Gilbert D., 143
Bathing
    before caring contact session, 110,
        252
    as encounter technique, 96, 105
Behavior, 230
    IPQ, calculating, 235
    in love, 249–251
    questionnaire, 231–235
    reinforcement, 242–243
    sexual, see Sexual behavior
    social, 243–248
Bell, Anita I., 189, 192
Bennis, Warren, 93
Berne, Eric, 42
Bidet, 35
Bindrim, Paul, 96
Bio-feedback, 84–85
Bioloops, 82
    breathing control, 86–88
    non-ejaculatory, 126–128
    orgasmic, for female, 123–126
    pressure, for ejaculatory control,
        121–122
    production, 83
    sexual, 88–92
Birth control, see Contraception
Bisexuality, 37, 40
Body bubble of space, 137
Body language, 137–138, 152, 158,
    220
Body lotions, 109, 111, 124
Body and mind, interdependence,
    216–218
Body movement, effect on mood,
    102
Bonding, pair, 26–27
Bottle feeding, 188–189
Bowers, Faubion, 44
Brain-wave bio-feedback, 84–85
Brain
    old, burdens of, 68–69
    response to thought loops, 81
    uniqueness of, 80–81
Breast feeding, 188–189
Breasts
    commercial exploitation of, 19

growth of, 19
    male envy of, 20, 21
    self-examination for lumps, 54
    stimulation of, 19
Breathing, control over, 86–88
Brothers, Joyce, 153
Brown, Barbara, 81, 84

C

Cancer, examination for, 55
Caressing, 109–117
    of female by male, 111–114
    of male by female, 115–117
    penis, 115
    varying, 112
Caring contact, 109–117, 125, 129,
    136
Central nervous system, 14–15, 84
Cervix, examination for cancer, 54
Chancres, 62
Chancroid, 63
Childbirth
    difficult, as handicap for child,
        188
    effect on intimacy, 165–167
    separation of husband and wife
        during, 166–167, 227
    vaginal injury during, 65
Childhood
    IPQ, calculating, 180
    need for intimacy, 3–4
    parents' disapproval of sexuality
        in, 45–46
    questionnaire, 176–181, 187–195
    seduction or rape in, 194
    self-image formation in, 187–188
    sex role training in, 37, 43–44
Chromosomes, sex, 11
Cigarette smoking, and fear of emo-
        tions, 221–222
Circumcision, 51–60
    effect on sensitivity of glans, 258
Climacteric, male and female, 167–
        168
Climax, see Orgasm
Clitoris
    caressing surrounding tissue, 113
    erection, 89
    glans, 35
    orgasm, 1, 2, 252

Clitoris (*cont'd*)
  prepuce, smegma under, 58
  stimulation of, 253, 254
Coca-Cola, douching with, 18
Coitus
  and advancing age, 259–260
  anal, 28
  clitoral stimulation during, 253, 254
  interruptus, 17, 26, 259
  oral, 28
  painful, 56–60
  and penis size, 24–25
  positions for, 117–119, 126, 256
  during pregnancy, 166
  prohibited in first caring contact sessions, 110
  reservatus, 83
  and vaginal size, 24
Color changes in vulva, during sexual excitement, 25
Commission on Pornography and Obscenity, Report of, 47
Communication
  by body and voice, 220
  inability, and drug use, 221
  and reading, 245
Communes, 148–149, 228
  marriage in, 277
Compatibility
  profile, 272–275
  sexual, 271–275
Computer dating services, 50
Concentration, free, 69, 71
  mutual, for couples, 72–73
Conception
  asexual, 276
  control of, 16–18, 57–58, 258–259
Condom, 17
Condyloma acuminata, 64
Constantine, Larry and Joan, 148
Constipation, psychosomatic, 217
Contraception, 15–18
  coitus interruptus, 259
  of future, 276
  intra-uterine device, 16–17
  oral, 16, 57
  prohibitions on, 227
  realistic attitude toward, 250
  rhythm method, 17

  vasectomy, 258
Cortex, cerebral, 69
Coué, Emile, 74
Courtesy in marriage, 154–155
Cunnilingus, 256

D

Daisy chains, 142
Decisions, making, 101, 219
Deodorants, feminine hygiene, 58
Dependency, 218–219, 224
Depression, mental and physical symptoms, 217
Diabetes mellitus, sexual inadequacy due to, 66–67
Diaphragm
  in breathing control, 87
  pelvic, *see* Pubococcygeus muscle
Diaphragm, contraceptive, 17
Dickinson, 89
Dilators, for vaginal opening, 56
Dildo, 34
Divorce
  peak time for, 140
  rate of, 50
  societal attitude toward, 227–228
Douching
  as contraceptive method, 18
  disturbing vaginal acidity, 58
Doyle, Emma Lee, 230
Drugs
  abuse, and inability to communicate, 221
  causing sexual inadequacy, 66
  use in adolescence, significance, 198
Dyspareunia, 56–60
  after hysterectomy, 66

E

Ejaculation
  control, *see* Ejaculatory control
  delaying, 6
  inability, bioloop for, 126–127
  premature, *see* Ejaculatory control
Ejaculatory control
  pressure bioloop for, 121–122
  problems in, 201–202, 259

Ejaculatory control (*cont'd*)
  pubococcygeus muscle in, 92
  Tantric writings on, 78–79
Elimination, and anxiety, 190
Ellis, Albert, 199
Embryology, similarities of male and
  female, 11–12
Emotions
  clues to, 100
  communicating, 221
  confused with judgments, 104
  fear of, and cigarette smoking, 222
  effect on hormone production, 14
  honest reporting, 104
  real, coping with, 100–103
  suppression by male, 8
Empathy, 222
Encounter groups, 93, 95–97, 225
  for couples, 103–105
  criticisms of, 94–95
  nude, 94, 96–97
  what happens, 97–100
Encounters, brief, 131–139
Endometriosis, 66
Enemas, emotional effect, 190
Erection
  achieving, bioloop for, 128–130
  clitoral, 88–89
  mechanism of, 89
  of nipples, 19
  restoring of, 255
  subsiding, causes of, 255
Estrogens
  effects of, 14
  in male, 14
Exercises, for expelling anger, 101
Extramarital activity, *see* Infidelity
Extrasensory perception, 222
  between intimate partners, 151–
    152

F

Families of future, 276–278
Fantasies, 123, 155
  accompanying masturbation, 34
  and love at first sight, 248
Fear
  of failure by woman, 126
  of impotence, 259
  of pregnancy, 251

Fecal matter, genital infections due
  to, 59
Feel and touch exercises, *see* Caring contact
Fellatio, 256
Female sex, downgrading of, 43–44
Female sexual response, 113–114
  aid on part of male, 254
  faulty patterns of, 7
  in homosexual encounters, 41
  orgasmic bioloop, 122–126
  repression by cultural restrictions,
    195
  society's attitude toward, 228–229
Female-inferior coital position, 117
  modification of, 125–126
Female-superior coital position, 117–
    118, 125, 127, 129–130
Fibrosis, 66
Fighting, constructive aspects of,
    161, 162–163, 250
Foreplay, 125
  See also Caring contact
Frenulum, pressure for ejaculatory
  control, 121
Freud, Sigmund, 21–23
Friedman, Meyer, 85
Fromm, Erich, 224

G

Genitalia
  awareness through thought loops,
    77, 88
  caressing, 111–116
  cleansing, 58
  embryology, 11–12
  incorporating into self-image, 25–
    26
  oral stimulation, 256
  See also Penis, Testicles, Vagina,
    etc.
Ginsburg, Benson E., 30
Glans clitoris, stimulating, 35
Glans penis
  caressing, 115
  effect of circumcision on, 258
  manipulation, 34
Goal-oriented performance in sexual
  functioning, 1–2, 6–7, 106–108,
    117, 142–143, 229, 251

Goldstein, Michael J., 46
Gonorrhea, 61–62
Granuloma inguinale, 64
Greeting, nonverbal, 103
Group marriage, 148, 277

H

Habits, building, 243
Harlow, Harry F., 3
Heart disease
  personality type prone to, 85
  and sexual activity, 67
  and suppression of emotions by
    male, 8
Hegar dilators, 56
Hermaphrodites, and gender of rear-
    ing, 12–13
Hoffman, Martin, 37
Homosexuality, 32, 147, 199
  attitudes toward, 36–37, 225
  female, 22, 40–41, 143
  myths about, 38
  preventing, 37
  as way of life, 38–41
Hooker, Evelyn, 36
Hormones, sexual, 14–16
  replacement, 66
Hostility
  coexisting with love, 49, 161–163,
    249
  see also Anger
Hymen, 55
  tags of tissue causing pain, 57
Hypochondria, 217
Hysterectomy
  dyspareunia after, 66
  and sexual capacity, 259

I

Illegitimacy, incidence of, 47
Impotence
  and aging, 168
  bioloop for correcting, 128–130
  causes of, 7, 249
  and diabetes, 66
  and drugs, 66
  fear of, 259
  premature ejaculation and, 259
  selective, 271

Imprinting, 150–151
Incest, 28
Independence, 218–219
Infections, genital, 58–59
Infidelity, 141
  and dependency of partner, 219
  incidence of, 140
  male, during wife's pregnancy, 166
  in menopausal years, 270
Institute for Sex Research, 38, 147
Intercourse, see Coitus
Interests, sharing, 136–137
Intimacy
  body barriers to, 53–67
  declining interest in, 266
  profile, charting, 261
  spiral, 159–169
Intimacy Potential Quotient, 173–
    175
  adolescent, 181–186, 194–202
  attitudes, calculating, 212–213
  calculation of score, 260
  childhood, 176–181, 187–195
  evaluating, 187–202, 214–230
  profiles, 261, 275
  similar, in partners, 174, 221, 268
  temperament, 203–207
Intrauterine device, 16
Intromission, readiness for, 116, 117
Irritability, 217
Israel, L., 84

J

Jealousy, 250
  of children for marital love, 193
  in marriage, 164–165
  and self-hatred, 50
  and swinging, 143
Johnson, Virginia E., 6, 107, 132,
    189, 198, 230, 259
Judgments, confused with emotions,
    105

K

Kamia, Joe, 84
Kant, Harold S., 46
Karezza, 83
Kegal, 90

Kibbutz, 228
Kinsey, Alfred E., 36, 38, 41, 140, 198
Klemer, Richard, Dr. and Mrs., 158

L

Labia minora
    development, 12
    during sexual excitement, 25, 88
Lesbianism
    attitude toward penis in, 21
    orgasms in, 41
    at swinging parties, 143
    as way of life, 40–41
Levinson, Boris, 4, 191
Levitsky, Abraham, 132
Libido, see Bisexuality, Sexual desire
Liddell, 85
Loneliness, 133
Lotions, body, 109, 111, 124
Love
    in adolescence, 201
    behavior in, 248–251
    coexisting with hostility, 49–50, 161–162, 249–250
    confused with sex, 47–48
    equated with food, 216
    expectations of, 249
    hazards in today's world, 51
    marital, jealousy of children, 193
    reasons for, 49–50
Love affair, ending, 139
Lubrication
    insufficient, 57
    use in caressing, 113
Lymphogranuloma venereum, 64

M

Magazines, men's and women's, 245
Maginnis, Patricia, 17
Manipulation in marriage, 153
Marriage
    adolescent, 47
    age at, 27
    and biological pair bond, 26–27
    coping with jealousy in, 164–165
    courtesy in, 154–155
    duration of, 27

fighting in, 161, 162–163, 215
    form in future, 276–277
    group, 148, 277
    growing apart in, 152–153, 156–157
    and imprinting, 150–151
    intimacy spiral in, 159–169
    money arguments in, 156–157
    monogamous, alternatives to, 148–149, 228, 277
    priorities in, 153–155
    valid reasons for, 49
    woman's choice, 138
Marsh, Earle M., 29
Massaging, 111
Masters, William H., 6, 107, 132, 189, 198, 230, 259
Masturbation, 28
    in adolescence, 198–199
    by animals, 29–30
    considered sinful, 33–34
    by female, 36–37
    by male, 33–34
    mechanical devices for, 34–35
    mutual, 199
    as preparation for intimacy, 253
    value of, 33
Mate swapping, see Swinging
Menninger, W. C., 217
Menopause, 167–168
    infidelity and, 270
    and sexual capacity, 259
Middle-aged crisis in men, 167–168
Millett, Kate, 22
"Missionary" position, 257
Money, relation to sex life, 156–157
Monogamy, alternatives to, 148–149, 228, 277
Monotony, producing neurotic behavior, 85
Mood, altered by body movement and stance, 102
Muscles
    diaphragm, 87
    genital, exercising, 256
    pubococcygeus, 89, 90, 91–92, 118, 124–125
    urethral, 90–91
Myths about sex, 257–259

N

National Organization for Women, 148
Nipples, erection of, 19
Nondemanding physical contact, *see* Caring contact
Nudity, in encounter groups, 94, 96–97

O

Ointment, anesthetizing, coating penis with, 254
Onanism, 32–33
Oral-genital contact, 255–256
Orgasm
  bioloop, for female, 122–126
  clitoral, 1, 2, 253
  during pregnancy, 166
  faking, 229
  female, 113–114
  in Lesbian relationships, 40
  male, 116
  manual stimulation to, 113, 116, 127
  multiple, 2, 114, 255
  mutual, 1, 254
  oral stimulation to, 116–117, 126–127, 256
  as performance goal, 1, 2
  relieving premenstrual and menstrual discomfort, 15
  vaginal, 1

P

Pair bonding, and marriage, 27
Papanicolaou tests, 54
Parents
  adoptive, 191
  attachment to, and choice of partner, 249
  attitude toward adolescents, 197
  attitude toward children, 188, 191–192
  attitude toward sex, 193–194
  disapproval of children's sexuality, 45–46, 193
  negative judgments, effect on young adults, 42–43

  violence of, 191
Penetration, readiness for, 117, 118
Penis
  caressing, 115
  coating with anesthetizing ointment, 254
  effect of circumcision on sensitivity, 258
  envy, by female, 22–23
  erection, 89, 127–130, 255
  frenulum, 116
  glans, 34, 116, 258
  head, 116
  shaft, 116
  size of, 24–25, 258
Perls, Fritz, 219
Perineometer, 90
Pets, 191
Phelan, Lana Clark, 17
Pill, the
  effects of, 16–17
  suppressing sexual excitement, 57–58
Poland, Jefferson, 146, 147
Pornography, 147
  educational function of, 46–47
Positions, coital, 117–119, 125–126, 256
Possessiveness, 164
Potency bioloop, 128–130
Pregnancy
  adolescent, 47
  effect on intimacy, 165–166
  fear of, 251
  sex during, 166
  test-tube, 276
Premenstrual tension, relief of, 14–15
Primates
  masturbation, 29
  prostitution among, 31
Prior, Deborah D., 189, 192
Profile
  compatibility, 272–275
  IPQ, 261, 275
Prostatitis, 60
Prostitution, among primates, 31
Psychosomatic ailments, 102–103
Psychosomatic problems, 215–218

Pubococcygeus muscles, 89, 90
  in ejaculatory control, 91, 92
  training, for female, 124–125
  use in coitus, 118

Q

Questionnaire, 176–186, 203–212, 231–235, 236–241

R

Rape, 31
  of child, consequences, 194
Rectal pain, in male, 60
Reik, Theodor, 49
Relatives, importance of, 191–192
Relaxation, 86–87
Religious background, effect of, 192
Reproductive tract embryology, 11–12
Reserpine, 66
Reuben, David, 18, 229
Reverse effect, law of, 74, 75
Rhythm method of birth control, 17
Rice-Wray, Edris, 18
Rigidity of personality, 197
Rimmer, Robert, 148
Rohmer, F., 84
Role playing
  in initial contacts between sexes, 165–166, 168
  by male and female, 5–7
Roles, sexual, 8–9, 151
  and attitudes toward opposite sex, 226–227
  childhood training in, 12–13, 43–44
  devalued, 192
  stereotyping, 193
Runciman, Alex, 43

S

Scent, sexual importance of, 109
Schutz, William C., 100
Scrotum
  caressing, 115
  changes in response to anxiety, 189
Seduction of child by adult, 194

Self-esteem
  building, 164
  destruction in adolescence, 197
Self-hatred, as cause of jealousy, 50
Self-image, 134–135
  formation in childhood, 187–188
Senses, 219–220, 246
Sensitivity, separation from sex, 106
Sensitivity groups, see Encounter groups
Sex
  assignment of, 12
  attitudes toward, 225–226, 227–230
  conflict about, 250
  drive, individual differences in, 271, 274
  importance to physical well-being, 53
  negative attitudes of parents, 193–194
  and money, 156–157
  organs, see Genitalia
  relations, see Coitus
  roles, see Roles, sexual
  separated from sensitivity, 106
Sexual athlete, 1, 229
Sexual behavior
  of animals, 29–31
  and ignorance, 252
  IPQ, calculating, 241
  questionnaire, 237–241
  restrictions on, 28, 32
Sexual desire
  and age, 168, 259–260
  individual differences in, 250, 270–271
Sexual Freedom League, 146–148
Sexual functioning
  adult, and childhood intimacy, 3–5
  bioloops for, 88–92
  in old age, 168, 259–260
  performance goals in, 1–2, 6–7, 106–108, 117, 143–144, 229, 252
Sexual jock, 1, 270
  fate of, 8–9
Sharpy, Adrien, 24
Siblings, 191

Single people
  brief encounters between, 131–139
  exclusion from swinging parties, 145
  society's attitude toward, 50, 228
Smegma, causing genital irritation, 58, 59
Smell, sense of, 220
Spermicidal agents, 17–18
Squeeze technique for ejaculatory control, 121–123
Stance
  effect on mood, 102
  effect of self-image on, 133–134
Stroebel, Charles F., 189, 192
Stova, J., 84
"Sunday neurosis," 244
Swapping, *see* Swinging
Swinging, 140–149
  parties, 141–144
  recreational, 145–146
  Utopian, 146–148
Sympathetic nervous system, 68–69
Synanon, 95
Syphilis, 63–64

T

Taste, sense of, 221
Temperament, 214
  and bodily condition, 215–217
  IPQ, 207
  questionnaire, 203–207
Testicles
  caressing, 114
  development, 12
  retraction at end of defecation, 189
Testosterone, 14
T groups, *see* Encounter groups
Thought loops, 68, 110, 129
  advanced, 75–78
  for correcting self-image, 133–134
  definition, 69
  for genital awareness, 76–77, 88, 123
  mutual training in, 72–74
  producing alpha waves, 83
  psychosomatic changes due to, 78–79

  response of brain to, 81
  training in use of, 69–70
Thumb wrestling, 104
Tissot, Dr., 32–33
Toilet training anxieties, 189
Touch, sense of, 221
Transactional analysis, 224–226
Trichomonads, 59
Trueblood, Elton, 215

U

Urethra, smooth muscles of, 90–91
Uterus, male envy of, 20–21

V

Vagina
  acidity of, 58
  atrophy, 66
  cleansing, 58
  damage during childbirth, 65
  dilation of, 55–56
  expansion of, 24
  infections, 58–59
  lubrication, 57, 113
Vaginismus, 55–56, 189
Vajroli, 91
Vasectomy, 258–259
Venereal diseases, 61–64
Vibrator, 123–125
Vincent, Jane, 43
Violence, 192
Voice quality, and personality, 221
Voyeurs, at swinging parties, 142

W

Womb envy, 21–23
Womb pool, 96, 105
Women's Liberation movement, 5, 97
Wrestling, 104

Y

Yoga, 68, 82–83, 91

Z

Zimmerman, Robert R., 3